AMERICAN
LATHE BUILDERS
1810 – 1910

AMERICAN LATHE BUILDERS
1810 – 1910

Kenneth L. Cope

ASTRAGAL PRESS
Mendham New Jersey

Library of Congress Control Number 2001090406
International Standard Book Number 1-879335-99-9

Cover design by Donald Kahn

Published by
THE ASTRAGAL PRESS
5 Cold Hill Road, Suite 12
P.O. Box 239
Mendham, New Jersey 07945-0239

Manufactured in the United States of America

DEDICATION

Dedicated to the men and women of the American machine tool industry. Often working under very difficult conditions, they made the tools that made the machines that made the United States the envy of the industrial world.

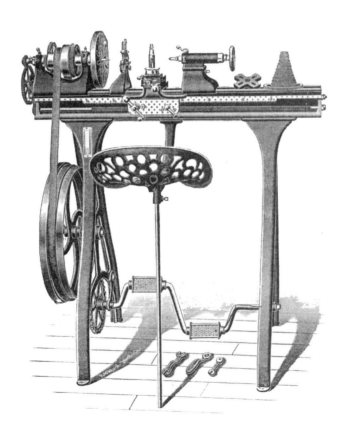

ACKNOWLEDGMENTS

Heartfelt thanks are extended to all those who helped make this book as complete as it is. Many people sent material from catalogs, city directories, and contemporary magazines from their collections or from sources to which they had access.

Special thanks to:

Ken Kranzusch whose machine tool catalog collection proved invaluable.

- Frank Morrison who scoured the Fitchburg, Massachusetts, Public Library and Fitchburg Historical Society.

- Phil Platt who did the same at Worcester, MA.

- Bob Vogel who tapped the machine tool catalog resources of the Smithsonian.

- The staff of the Milwaukee Public Library who never seemed to tire of hauling heavy, bound volumes of "American Machinist," "Machinery," "Iron Age," and other, more obscure, periodicals.

- Dozens of other librarians scattered across the United States who were unfailingly polite and helpful when I called.

INTRODUCTION

This work is not meant to be a history of the lathe. It is meant to bring to light the pioneer builders of the American metalworking lathe and to illustrate, as far as possible, their products. Many of the builders listed are well known and a few are still operating; others are obscure, and some are known only from a single advertisement placed in a contemporary magazine.

Information and illustrations have been gleaned from such sources as city directories, records of sales to the U.S. government, contemporary publications including AMERICAN ARTISAN, AMERICAN MACHINIST, AMERICAN MANUFACTURER, IRON AGE, MACHINERY, MECHANICS, and SCIENTIFIC AMERICAN magazines, and a large number of catalogs issued by lathe builders and dealers.

To put the entries into context, perhaps we need to start with a short definition of the lathe, such as the following offered in a 1900 publication: "The Lathe is a machine for working metals, wood, or other substance by causing the material to revolve with greater or less speed, according to the nature of the material and work to be performed, before a tool which is held at rest."

Illustrating the popular belief of the time that the lathe was the King of machine tools, the same publication went on to say: "It is generally understood that an expert lathe hand, or turner, is deemed capable of operating a planer, drilling machine or any of the ordinary machine tools, whereas those who have learned to operate any or all of these machines would prove altogether inefficient if put to operate a lathe."

American metalworking lathes were made in a bewildering variety of types, each to meet a specific need that arose as manufacturing problems were encountered with new, larger, and more complex products. New types, when proven successful, were quickly copied by other lathe builders and earned their place alongside older types.

The following list, with short descriptions, will help the reader wade through references to the various forms of lathes named in the text. Note that all entries and descriptions apply to lathes produced during the period 1810-1910. Many of these lathe types were later abandoned, greatly modified, or became known by different names.

Axle Lathe—a heavy duty lathe designed to turn railroad car axles. It was made as a double lathe, for turning both ends in one set up, and a single lathe, for turning only one end.

Back Geared Lathe—a lathe in which the speed of the spindle can be reduced by a set of gears at the back of the headstock. This may be a double-gear or triple-gear mechanism.

Bench Lathe—a small lathe meant to be mounted on a bench. It was intended for small work, usually requiring considerable accuracy.

Brassworker's Lathe—see Fox Lathe.

Car Wheel Lathe—see Wheel Lathe.

Chain Lathe—an early form of engine lathe in which the tool slide was traversed by a chain and sprocket drive. It gave a poor feed, since the chain could not be kept tight, but was simple to make.

Chasing Lathe—see Screw-Cutting Lathe.

Chucking Lathe—a lathe in which the chuck or faceplate was of larger than usual diameter and the bed was shorter than usual. Some were equipped with turrets; others only with a cross slide. The chucking lathe was used for machining work held near the headstock rather than between centers.

Crankshaft Lathe—a lathe especially made to turn crankshafts. Many were arranged to drive the crankshaft from both ends to prevent distortion.

Edging Lathe—a special form of lathe used to trim the edges of spun metal parts made on spinning lathes. See entry for WATERBURY FARREL FOUNDRY & MACHINE CO. for an example.

Engine Lathe—a lathe with a slide rest actuated automatically to traverse the tool while cutting. Some also had power feed in the cross slide. In American practice, engine lathe size is specified in inches of swing, or the diameter of a cylinder that may be rotated between centers.

Origin of the term "engine lathe" is somewhat cloudy, but most agree that the name came about during the early 19th century when the term *engine* was applied to all types of machines and therefore an *engine lathe* was one used by machine builders. *Engine lathes* were also called *self-acting* lathes.

A near infinite variety of accessories and attachments were developed for the engine lathe. Many were offered to allow milling, gear cutting, shaping and other machining operations to be performed. Turrets, turret tool holders and a variety of other means to increase tooling flexibility were also offered. A number of others attachments were means to increase the swing of the lathe.

Extension Bed Gap Lathe—a lathe with a double form of bed, the upper section of which could be extended in order to create a gap for increasing the swing, and also the distance between centers.

Facing Lathe—a lathe with a large diameter faceplate, very short bed, and no provision for tail stock. They were used for facing large workpieces such as gear blanks.

Foot Lathe—a lathe driven by foot power.

Forge Lathe—a very heavy duty engine lathe designed to machine tough forgings. Most were made without a thread cutting mechanism.

Forming Lathe—a very heavy duty engine lathe designed to make unusually wide cuts with form tools. They were equipped with special slide rests and had very powerful drives.

Fox Lathe—a high speed, light duty lathe designed for the machining of brass and other soft metal workpieces. Fox lathes were supplied with a swinging tool post slide whose rear end was journaled to a rear mounted lead screw that gave a longitudinal feed when the slide was brought over to the front by means of a handle. These were also known as *brassworker's lathes*. See entry for AMERICAN TOOL & MACHINE CO. for a history.

Gap Lathe—a lathe with a gap formed in the bed in front of the headstock for the purpose of increasing the "swing," or maximum diameter, that could be revolved.

Hand Lathe—a lathe without a tool holding device, requiring that the cutting tool be held in the operator's hand. We now think of this type as only used for turning wood. However, metal turning, and even thread cutting, was commonly done with hand held tools until the late 19th century.

High Speed Lathe—an engine lathe designed to use the new high speed steel cutting tools introduced in the early 20th century. Taylor & White, makers of the new tool steel, required buyers to have a licence before they could use high speed steel cutting tools and issued licences only to firms using machine tools with proper rigidity and range of feeds and speeds. Taylor & White knew that the new tools would fail if used with inadequate machine tools and their business would suffer as a result. Lathe builders were quick to design new machines which met the Taylor & White standards. These new designs were the standard until the 1930s introduction of carbide cutting tools started another round of improved machine tools.

Locomotive Driving Wheel Lathe—see Wheel Lathe.

Monitor Lathe—a turret lathe with a round turret rotating on a vertical axis. The name originated from its similarity in appearance to the turret mounted on the Civil War ironclad USS Monitor. The term was popular from the mid-1860s to about 1890.

Pattern Lathe or Patternmaker's Lathe—a lathe specifically designed to machine wood and some soft metals used in patternmaking. Most were equipped with compound tool rests to allow the accurate machining required for patterns.

Polishing Lathe—see Speed Lathe.

Precision Lathe—usually a Bench Lathe capable of very accurate work and more expensive than ordinary bench lathes.

Pulley Lathe—a lathe specifically designed to machine pulleys and flywheels, including boring and reaming the hole and turning the face. Some were made to cut either crowned or flat faces.

Roll Lathe—a very heavy duty lathe designed to turn rolls used in steel rolling mills. They were notable for the use of extreme gear reductions in the drive mechanism.

Roughing Lathe—a lathe designed to rough cut workpieces that were finished by other means such as grinding. Developed during the early 20th century, the roughing lathe was used to increase production of high volume parts such as were found in the automobile industry.

Screw-Cutting Lathe—a lathe provided with a lead screw that caused the cutting tool to advance an accurate, predetermined amount for each rotation of the screw. A combination of the lead screw and change gears, which drove the lead screw, provided the ability to cut a variety of thread pitches.
    Some screw-cutting lathes were furnished with a number of demountable lead screws, one for each thread pitch to be cut. These were also called *chasing lathes*.

Screw Machine—see Turret Lathe.

Self-Acting Lathe—see Engine Lathe.

Shafting Lathe—an engine lathe specifically designed for production of shafting and other long, cylindrical parts. Such lathes tended to have a long bed and slide rest traverse distance in relation to the swing size and were equipped with special shafting tool rests. Some drove the workpiece from both ends to prevent problems due to torsional effects of long, small diameter workpieces.

Single Geared Lathe—a lathe in which the speed of spindle rotation is always the same as the cone.

Speed Lathe—a simple lathe, made without back gears, used for rotating parts rapidly for polishing, hand turning, or filing. They were supplied with a slide rest only as an option.

Spinning Lathe—a lathe designed to form shapes from rotating discs of thin metal with variously shaped tools that may be held in the hand or in the tool post of a slide rest. The forming process was often done on specially shaped mandrels. There was no cutting action.

Toolroom or Toolmaker's Lathe—a form of the engine lathe, usually 14" swing or less, furnished with extra attachments and made to higher accuracy standards than production lathes.

Turning Engine—an early name for metalworking lathes, probably applying primarily to engine lathes.

Turret Lathe—a lathe in which cutting tools for performing successive operations were held in a revolvable turret. Most turrets rotated on a vertical axis; some early types, however, were made with turrets that rotated on a horizontal axis.

Turret lathes were usually specified by the diameter and length of bar stock which could be fed through the headstock. Thus, a 2" x 24" turret lathe was designed to handle a maximum 2" diameter bar stock, up to 24" in length.

Small turret lathes, made for turning small parts from rods or bar stock, were often called *screw machines*. The term, as applied to a form of turret lathe, became obsolete when the automatic screw machine was developed.

Watchmaker's Lathe—a small, bench mounted lathe, usually foot powered, supplied with a variety of attachments for making small watch parts.

Wheel Lathe—a large lathe intended for turning locomotive driving wheels. Most were of double faceplate design, which held sets of driving wheels. Smaller designs were used for machining railroad car wheels.

Directory
of
Makers

AITCHISON, JAMES, Cleveland, OH

Maker, c1882-1886, of hand lathes and 13" turret lathes in freestanding (Fig.1) and bench (Fig.2) models. In 1884, Aitchison also offered small quick-opening chucks (Fig.3) which could be operated without stopping the machine.

NEW TURRET LATHE.   **Fig. 1**

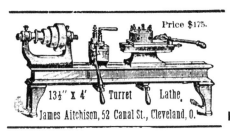

Price $175.

13½" x 4'   Turret   Lathe.
James Aitchison, 52 Canal St., Cleveland, O.   **Fig. 2**

Aitchison's New Lathe Chuck.   **Fig. 3**

ALCORN & AMES, Waltham, MA

A partnership of John Alcorn (1860-1938) and Bliss C. Ames (1867-1948) formed in 1898 to make small bench lathes for the Waltham watch industry. The partnership was dissolved in 1901. Alcorn then formed the ALCORN MACHINE CO. and Ames formed B.C. AMES CO.

ALCORN MACHINE CO., Waltham, MA

Formed by John Alcorn (1860-1938) in 1901 when the partnership of ALCORN & AMES was dissolved. Alcorn continued to make the line of precision bench lathes previously made by ALCORN & AMES.

ALDRICH & HAY, Lowell, MA, later
ALDRICH, WARREN, Lowell, MA, later
ALDRICH, TYNG & CO., Lowell, MA

A partnership of Warren Aldrich and James Hay, formed in 1840 to make engine lathes. The partnership dissolved in 1845. Aldrich continued business under his own name until 1853 when he formed a new partnership, ALDRICH, TYNG & CO., with Levi D. Tyng.

Aldrich patented engine lathe designs on March 15, 1853 and April 10, 1855 (shown below); Tyng patented his on March 7, 1854.

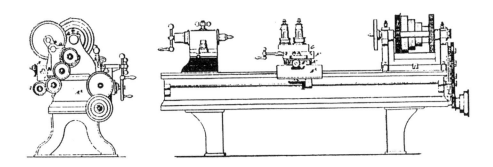

AMERICAN TOOL & MACHINE CO., Boston, MA

Formed in 1864 as successor to G.H. FOX & CO. Maker of brass workers' screw chasing lathes, patented January 3, 1854, by Joseph Nason (Fig.1). This became known as the *FOX* lathe, which was made in great variety well into the 20th century.

Production in 1884 included the square arbor brassworkers' lathe in several sizes (Fig.2) and the cabinet style *FOX* turret lathe, also in several sizes (Fig.3).

By 1900 production expanded to include *FOX* turret lathes in 18" (Fig.4), 20" (Fig.5), 24", and 26" (Fig.6) sizes; square arbor brass workers' lathes in 13" and 17" (Fig.7) sizes; and a set-over brass workers' hand lathe with 13" swing (Fig.8).

The firm continued the same products until at least 1916 and probably through World War I.

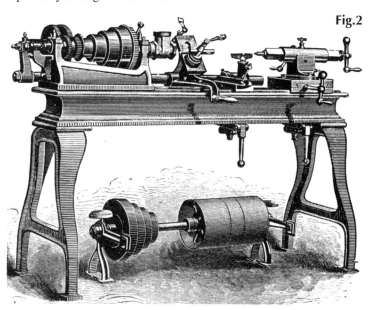

Fig.2

Fig.1

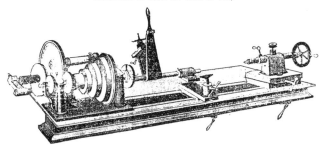

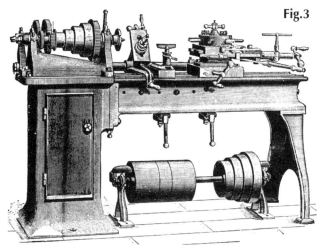

Fig.3

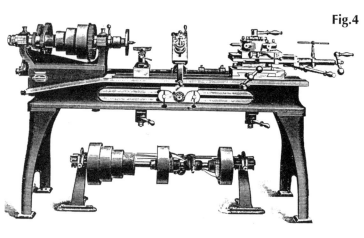

Fig.4

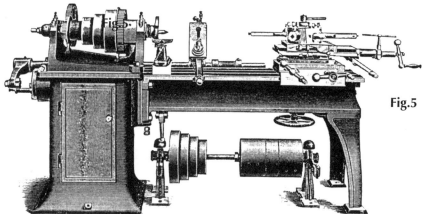

Fig.5

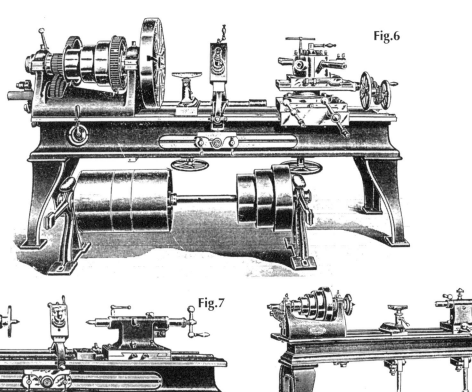

Fig.6

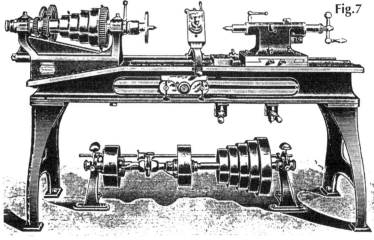

Fig.7

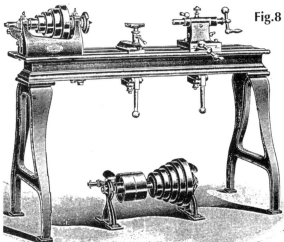

Fig.8

AMERICAN TOOL WORKS CO., Cincinnati, OH

Formed in 1898 by Franklin Alter (1831-1916), Albert B. Voorheis and Charles Davis (1853-1903) as a reorganization of the DAVIS & EGAN MACHINE TOOL CO., with an initial capitalization of $1,000,000. The new firm continued production of Davis & Egan designs, including engine lathes with 14" to 60" swings (Figs.1&2), milling machines, drilling machines, shapers and planers. Lathe production continued until the company went out of business in the 1970s.

Electrically driven 52" engine lathes were introduced in 1900. Motor speed was controlled by a reostat that "can be placed in any desirable location." A 24" electrically driven engine lathe (Fig.3) was introduced in 1902. This design used a four-speed motor and change gearing to obtain 16 spindle speeds.

New design 20" engine lathes with quick change feed gear boxes were introduced in 1903 in cone head (Fig.4) and geared head versions. They were made specifically for use with high speed steel cutting tools. 22" combination lathes (Fig.5), furnished with a separately powered drilling attachment for the turret, were introduced in 1904. In 1905, a new design of manufacturing turret lathe (Fig.6) was offered in several sizes. *(Illustrations continued on next page)*

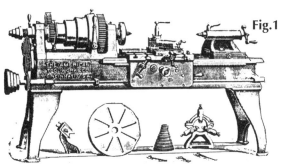

Fig.1

18-INCH STANDARD ENGINE LATHE.

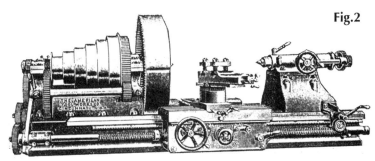

Fig.2

54 INCH SWING STANDARD LATHE.

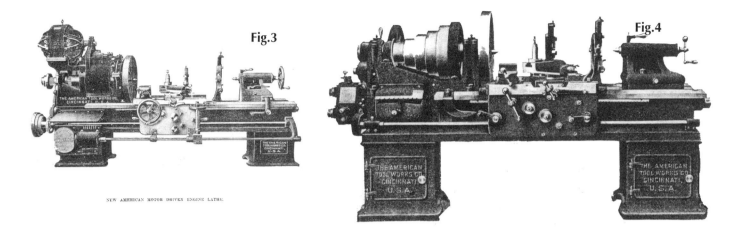

Fig.3

Fig.4

NEW AMERICAN MOTOR DRIVEN ENGINE LATHE.

Fig.5

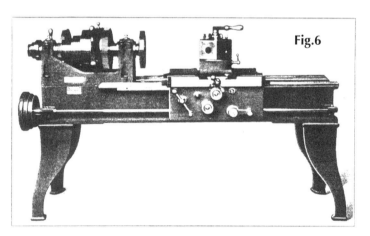

Fig.6

New Manufacturing Turret Lathe Built by the American Tool Works Company.

AMERICAN TURRET LATHE CO.,   Wilmington, DE, later Warren, PA

Formed in 1898 to make large turret lathes designed by Conrad M. Conradson (1861-1940) who had designed large turret lathes for the GISHOLT CO. 1889-1895. The firm moved to Warren, PA, in 1902 and was taken over by the GISHOLT CO. in 1905.

Production in 1900 included CONRADSON turret lathes in 20" (Fig.1), 24" (Fig.2), and 40" (Fig.3) sizes. An 18" semi-automatic turret lathe (Fig.4), with quick-change feeds selected by a large dial, was introduced in 1902. *(Illustrations next page)*

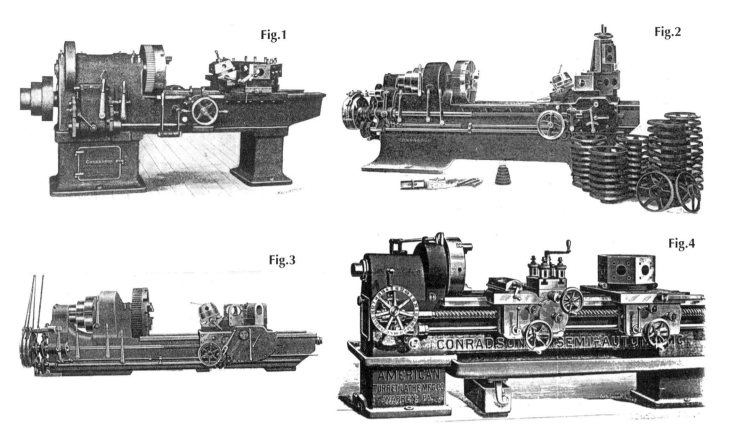

Fig.1

Fig.2

Fig.3

Fig.4

AMERICAN WATCH TOOL CO., Waltham, MA

A partnership of Ambrose Webster (1832-1894) and John E. Whitcomb, formed in 1876 as a reorganization of BALLOU & WHITCOMB. The firm specialized in small machinery for the Waltham watch making industry and operated until 1918 when it was merged into the Wade-American Tool Co. Products included small bench lathes (Fig.1) in 1880, 10" hand lathes (Fig.2) in 1881, and an improved machinists' model (Fig.3) introduced in 1882. A watchmakers' bench model, complete with a wide variety of attachments, (Fig.4) was offered in 1887. *(Illustrations continued on next page)*

Fig.1

American Watch Tool Co., Waltham, Mass.

MANUFACTURERS OF

MACHINERY

FOR

Watch and Clock Making,

AND

Special Tools and Machinery of all kinds.

The accompanying cut shows our No. 3, or Machinist Bench Lathe. This lathe was originally designed for the American Watch Co., and has been adopted by all American watch companies and by many clock companies of this country, and watch companies of England and Switzerland. All agree in pronouncing it the best lathe for small work ever made.

Fig.2

IMPROVED HAND LATHE.

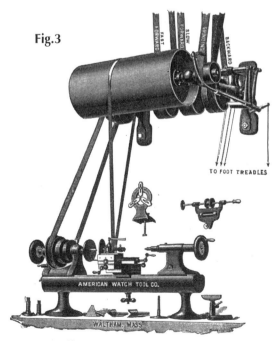

Fig.3

TO FOOT TREADLES

NEW MACHINISTS' BENCH LATHE.

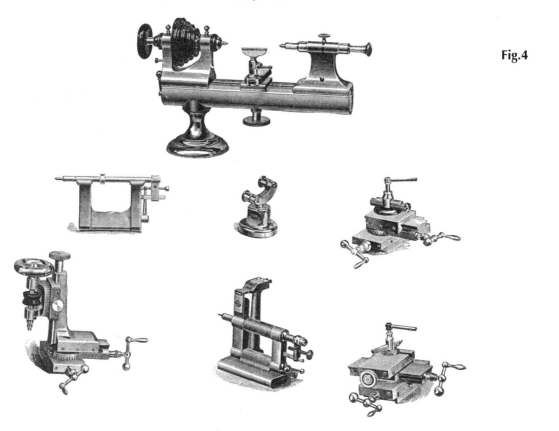

Fig.4

AMES CO., B.C., Waltham, MA

Formed by Bliss C. Ames (1867-1948) when the partnership of ALCORN & AMES was dissolved in 1901. Bliss continued to make a line of small bench lathes similar to those made by ALCORN & AMES. The 7" model shown below was made unchanged from 1901 until at least 1936. All lathe production ceased in 1946.

AMES MFG. CO., Chicopee Falls, MA

Founded in 1834 by James T. Ames (1810-1883) and his brother Nathan P. Ames, Jr. (1803-1847) to make cotton machinery and machine tools. Ames was one of the first machine tool builders to make and market a standard line of machine tools.

Machine tool production began as early as 1835 when a screw turning lathe and several milling machines were sold to Merrick, Agnew & Tyler, Philadelphia, PA. A "small screw lathe" was shipped to Harpers Ferry Armory in 1837.

From the 1850s through 1865 Ames was an important supplier of machine tools to the Springfield Armory. At the end of the Civil War, however, firearms, swords, sewing machines, etc., became important products. Machine tool production began to taper off and ceased soon after 1890. The firm was closed in 1898.

Lathe production included small engine lathes beginning in 1835. Much larger 27" engine lathes (Fig.1) and 90" engine lathes (Fig.2) were offered in 1885. Many lathes were equipped with the Hadley tool rest (Fig.3), patented October 29, 1872, which allowed fine vertical adjustment. *(Illustrations continued on next page)*

Fig.1

6

Fig.2

Fig.3

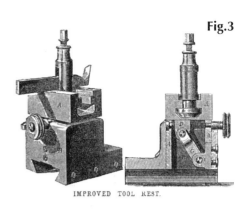

IMPROVED TOOL REST.

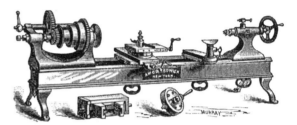

New Back-Geared Hand Lathe.

AMOR & BOWKER, New York, NY
Maker, in 1880, of small bench lathes such as that shown at right.

AMOSKEAG CO., Manchester, NH
The shops of this large maker of textile machinery, were erected in 1840. William A. Burke (1811-?) served as superintendent until leaving in 1845 to join the LOWELL MACHINE SHOP. The firm made a variety of machinery, including large engine and pit lathes. Both William B. Bement and Ira Gay were employed by Amoskeag early in their working lives.

ASHTON & CO., H., Middlefield, CT
Formed in 1845 to make 30,000 M1842 U.S. pistols under a contract granted to Henry Ashton. Stephen Fitch, a contractor to Ashton, designed and built a horizontal axis turret lathe in 1845 which is now considered to be the first turret lathe. The machine was examined and described in 1870 as part of a patent suit and was destroyed by a fire in 1879.

AUTOMATIC RAPID LATHE CO., Saco, ME
Formed in 1892 with a capital stock of $200,000. The sole product appears to have been Childs' Automatic Rapid Lathe, designed by Eugene Childs. The lathe was designed to maintain a constant surface speed as the cross feed moved from the outer edge of the workpiece to the center. As shown in the drawing below, it was mechanically very complicated and does not appear to have been successful.

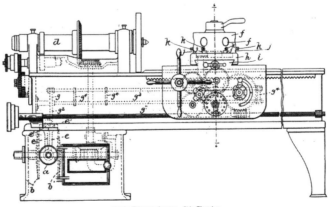

CHILDS TURRETT LATHE.—Side Elevation.

BACON, MURRAY, Philadelphia, PA
Maker, in 1872, of foot lathes and power lathes "with or without back gears."

BADGER & CO., A.M., Rochester, NY
Operated by Alfred M. Badger. Maker, in 1865, of "all kinds of machinists' tools." At least one engine lathe survives today. In 1869, his widow was advertising the business for sale.

BAGLEY, E.A., Worcester, MA
Inventor and maker of a screw machine with a manually rotated, horizontal axis turret, patented March 30, 1869. The machine, shown right, appears to have been made as late as 1880.

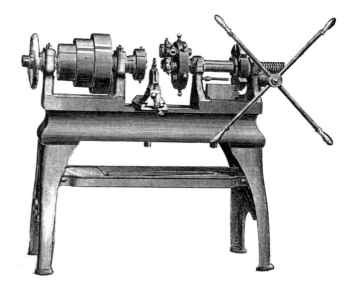

BAIRD MACHINERY CO., U., Pittsburgh, PA
A large Pittsburgh machinery dealer. The firm offered a variety of lathes and planers under its own name but probably made by others. Private label machines included a 26", double back geared, engine lathe introduced in 1899 and shown below.

BAKER MACHINE CORP., New Bedford, MA
Maker, in 1907, of the BAKER improved turret head shown at right. Made in two sizes, it was "applicable to any speed or engine lathe." By 1912, the unit was offered in slightly different form by S.S. Baker, Manf'r, Chicago, IL.

BALLOU MFG. CO., Hartford, CT
Founded in 1883 by George F. Ballou (1845-1935) to make small, 7" bench lathes (Fig.1) and 7" universal engine lathes (Fig.2). The firm went out of business in 1886, but production of the Ballou design lathe was continued by the WATERHOUSE ELECTRIC & MFG. CO. Ballou had previously made small lathes as part of the partnership of BALLOU & WHITCOMB, which operated 1872-1874. *(Illustrations on next page)*

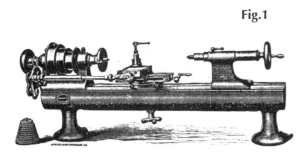

Fig.1

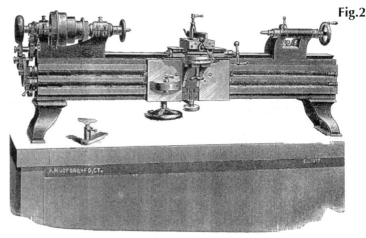

Fig.2

SMALL UNIVERSAL ENGINE LATHE.

BALLOU & WHITCOMB,   Waltham, MA

A partnership of George F. Ballou and John E. Whitcomb, formed in 1872 to make small lathes and other machinery for the Waltham watch making industry. Ballou sold out to Whitcomb in 1874 and the firm reorganized as the AMERICAN WATCH TOOL CO. in 1876.

BANCROFT & SELLERS,   Philadelphia, PA

A partnership of Edward Bancroft (?-1855) and his brothers-in-law William Sellers (1824-1905) and John Sellers, Jr. (1826-1906) formed in 1848. The firm was reorganized as WILLIAM SELLERS & CO. when Bancroft died in 1855. Products included engine lathes with a feed gear change design patented February 7, 1854, by Edward Bancroft and William Sellers.

BANCROFT & SON, N.W., Worcester, MA, later
BANCROFT & SMITH, Worcester, MA, later
BANCROFT & CO., W.F., Worcester, MA

A partnership of Nathan W. Bancroft and his son William F. Bancroft formed about 1880. By 1883, the firm became BANCROFT & SMITH, a partnership of William F. Bancroft and Harvey H. Smith. In 1884, the firm reorganized as W.F. BANCROFT & CO. All three firms made woolen machinery and light machinists' tools, including hand lathes (Fig.) and light engine lathes. The WOOD'S pulley lathe (Fig.) was introduced in 1892.

Hand Lathe, 10 Inch Swing, 4 Foot Bed.

Wood's Pulley Turning Machine.

(PATENTS PENDING.)

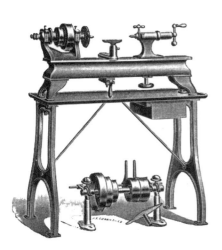

Fig.1

Fig.2

BARDONS & OLIVER, Cleveland, OH

A partnership of George C. Bardons (1860-1924) and John G. Oliver (1861-1939), formed October 1, 1891, to make turret lathes. Both Bardons and Oliver had previously worked for the WARNER & SWASEY CO., Bardons as superintendent and Oliver as chief draftsman.

Early products included 14" turret lathes (Fig.1) introduced in 1892 and improved turret lathes (Fig.2) introduced in 1894 and made in six sizes from 15" to 22". 1903 offerings included brassworkers' lathes (Fig.3) made in 14", 16", 18" and 20" sizes and screw machines made in six sizes from 13" to 21" (Fig.4).

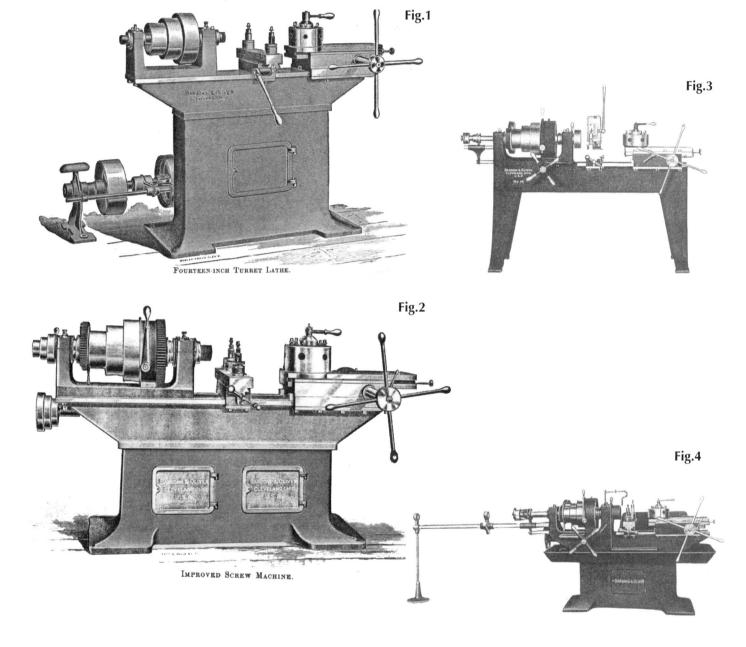

Fig.1

FOURTEEN-INCH TURRET LATHE.

Fig.3

Fig.2

IMPROVED SCREW MACHINE.

Fig.4

BARKER & CHARD MACHINE TOOL CO., Cincinnati, OH

Formed in 1897 by William Barker (1853-1915), Nicholas D. Chard (1863-1942), and William H. Burtner. Barker had been a partner in LODGE, BARKER & CO. from 1880 to 1886 and operated WILLIAM BARKER & CO. from 1886 until his death in 1915.

The sole product appears to have been engine lathes, with optional turrets that could be mounted on the carriage. The 18" size is shown on next page. Short lived, the firm closed in 1901. Chard then became superintendent of the LODGE & SHIPLEY MACHINE TOOL CO.

(Illustration continued on next page)

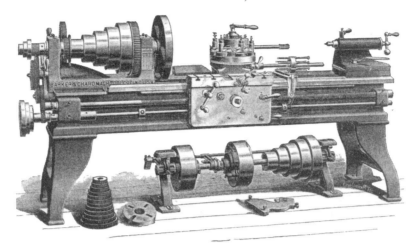

THE BARKER & CHARD LATHE TURRET ATTACHMENT.

BARKER & CO., T.L., Fitchburg, MA

A partnerhip of T.L. Barker and A. Brigham. Maker, in 1869, of "engine and hand lathes."

BARKER & CO., WILLIAM, Cincinnati, OH

Formed in 1886 by William Barker (1853-1915) after selling his share of LODGE, BARKER & CO. Barker served as president until his death in 1915. His three sons then continued the business, probably through World War I.

The firm made a variety of small machines for the valve industry including small lathes of the FOX brassworking type (Fig.1). A lathe center grinder (Fig.2) was introduced in 1890 and became a staple product for many years. Lathe production appears to have ceased about 1900. Barker was also a partner in BARKER & CHARD MACHINE TOOL CO. from 1897 to 1901.

Fig.1

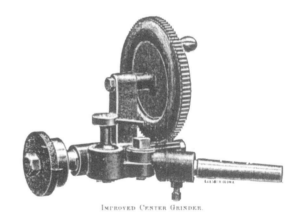

IMPROVED CENTER GRINDER.

Fig.2

BARKER & STARRETT, Philadelphia, PA

A partnership of John Barker and James Starrett. Maker of "small lathes for steam or foot power" in 1877.

BARNES CO., B.F., Rockford, IL

Founded in 1899 by Benjamin F. Barnes (1857-1919) after leaving his brothers' company, W.F. & JOHN BARNES, where he had been superintendent for 25 years. Products were primarily drilling machines, but he also offered 9" and 11" screw cutting lathes in countershaft (Fig.1) and foot power (Fig.2) models.

In June, 1907, Barnes sold his firm to a group that reorganized as the Rockford Drilling Machine Co. He then organized the BARNES DRILL CO. *(Illustrations continued on next page)*

11

Fig.1

11-inch Power Lathe

Fig.2

9-inch Foot Power Lathe

BARNES DRILL CO., Rockford, IL

Formed in June, 1907, by Benjamin F. Barnes (1857-1919) and J.E. Andress (1876-1956). Barnes had previously been the owner of B.F. BARNES CO. which made engine lathes and drilling machines.

The company's primary products were drilling machines, but it also made 12/22" sliding extension gap lathes *(at right)* beginning in 1907. An electrically driven model of the same lathe was offered in 1910 and a larger 22/36" size by 1914.

12-22 inch Sliding Extension Gap Lathe

The advantages of the Sliding Gap Feature of this Lathe are apparent. It not only increases the swing of the lathe and the distance between centers, but permits the width of the gap to be varied to suit requirements of the work.

BARNES, W.F. & JOHN, Rockford, IL, later
BARNES CO., W.F. & JOHN, Rockford, IL

Formed in 1872 by William F. Barnes (1841-1930) and his brother John (1833-1916) to make scroll saws and other foot-power machinery. The two brothers were joined by a third brother, Benjamin F. (1857-1919) in 1874. W.F. Barnes was elected president when the firm was incorporated as W.F. & JOHN BARNES CO. in 1884 but sold out in 1906. John Barnes was then elected president, serving until his death in 1916.

Early lathe models, No.1 through No.3, all introduced in 1876, were designed for cutting wood. Metal cutting lathes began with the 7" swing, No.4, introduced in 1876 (Fig.1) with a bench seat and velocipede drive. By 1884, the No.4 was offered with a bucket seat and either treadle or velocipede drive (Fig.2).

About 1899, the 9" swing No. 4 1/2, screw cutting lathe was introduced in a bench model (Fig.3) and a foot-power model (Fig.4). The 9" swing No.5 lathe (Fig.5) was introduced in 1877. A true engine lathe, it was equipped with power feed. By 1900 the swing had been increased to 11" (Fig.6). The 13" swing No. 5 1/2 model (Fig.7) was introduced about 1900 as a larger, improved version of the No.5.

The 12" swing No.6 lathe (Fig.8) was introduced about 1880 in both treadle and velocipede models. By 1900, the swing had been increased to 13" and it was offered in bed lengths up to 10'.

The last lathe offering was the No.13 introduced in 1901. It was identical to the No.6 lathe but with the addition of power cross feed patented June 19, 1894, and was offered in both foot-power (Fig.9) and countershaft (Fig.10) models. *(Illustrations continued on next page)*

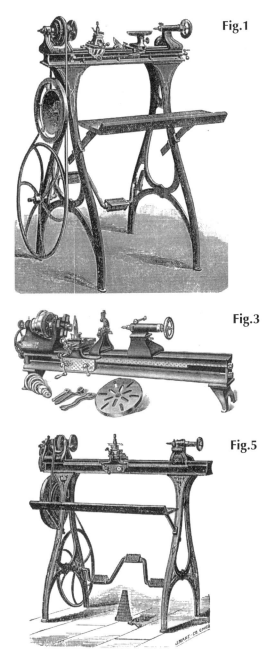

Fig.1

Fig.3

Fig.5

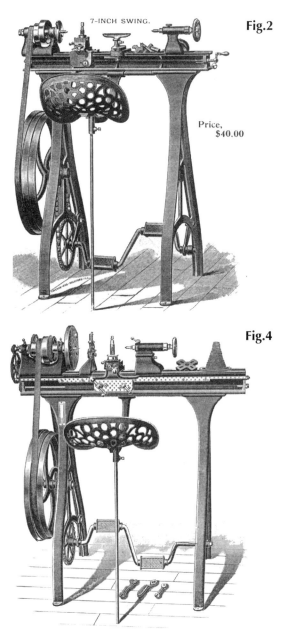

Fig.2

7-INCH SWING.

Price, $40.00

Fig.4

Fig.6

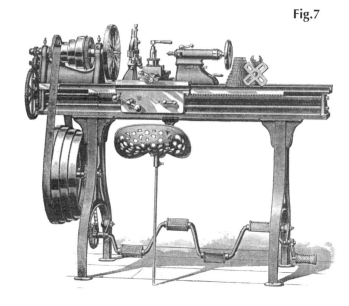
Fig.7

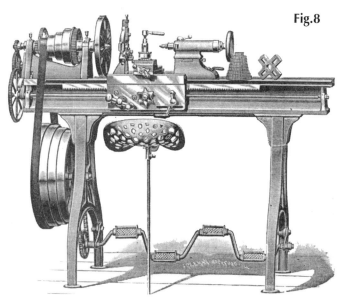
Fig.8

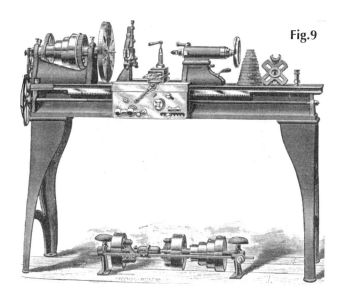
Fig.9

BARNETT, OSCAR, Newark, NJ
Maker of lathes, shapers, and presses c1865.

BEAMAN & SMITH, Providence, RI
Formed in 1886 as a partnership of Elmer A. Beaman (1846-1921) and George H. Smith. Milling machines were the primary product but the firm also made a variety of lathes c1890-1891, including 16" engine lathes (Fig.1) and 21" combinaton turret lathes (Fig.2).
(Illustrations continued on next page)

Fig.1

Fig.2

BELLOWS & WHITCOMB, Worcester, MA

A partnership of Ephraim H. Bellows and Bryon Whitcomb, formed in 1865 and dissolved in 1868. The firm was primarily a steam engine builder but also made "lathes, planers, drills, and shaping machines."

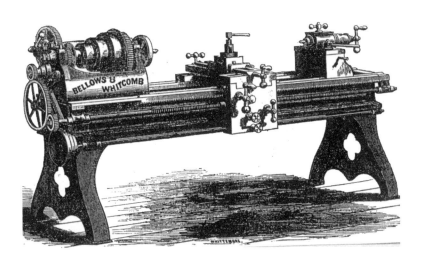

BEMENT & DOUGHERTY, Philadelphia, PA, later
BEMENT & SON, WILLIAM B., Philadelphia, PA, later
BEMENT, MILES & CO., Philadelphia, PA

A partnership of William B. Bement (1817-1897) and James Dougherty (1815-1900) formed in 1856 as a reorganization of BEMENT, DOUGHERTY & THOMAS. Bement had been a noted designer of machine tools for the LOWELL MACHINE SHOP 1845-1851. Products included large vertical lathes (Fig.1).

In 1870 Bement and his son, Clarence S. (1843-1923), formed a new company, WILLIAM B. BEMENT & SON, that operated as the proprietor of the INDUSTRIAL WORKS. Products included large engine lathes (Fig.2-4), axle cut-off and centering lathes (Fig.5), and single-end axle lathes (Fig.6) for the railroad industry. *(continued on next three pages)*

The firm reorganized as BEMENT, MILES & CO. on May 1, 1885, when it merged with Frederick B. Miles' MACHINE TOOL WORKS. Products continued to include large engine lathes including a 63" model (Fig.7).

On August 15, 1899, the company merged with the NILES TOOL WORKS and POND MACHINE TOOL CO. to form the NILES-BEMENT-POND CO. BEMENT, MILES & CO. continued operation as a division.

Production in 1903 included 63" heavy duty forge lathes, 72" motor driven engine lathes (Fig.8), single axle lathes (Fig.9), double axle lathes (Fig.10), 51" driving wheel lathes (Fig.11), 100" and 125" crankshaft lathes (Fig.12), and 42" facing lathes (Fig.13).

(Illustrations continued on next three pages.)

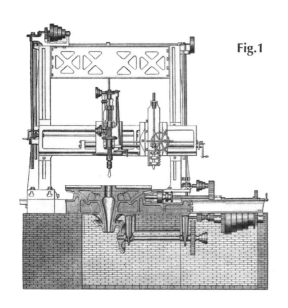

Fig.1

Fig.2

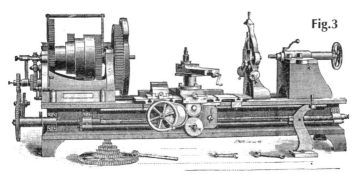

Fig.3

Fig.4

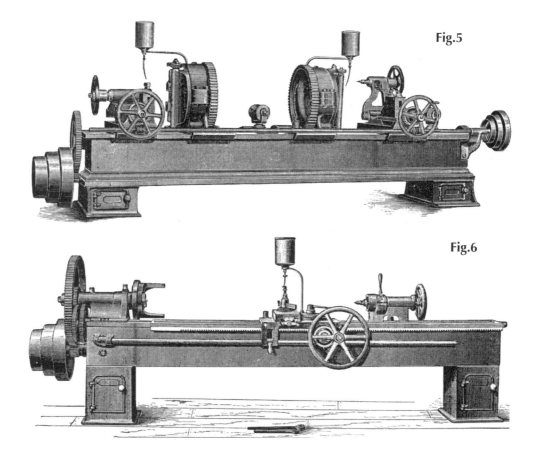

Fig.5

Fig.6

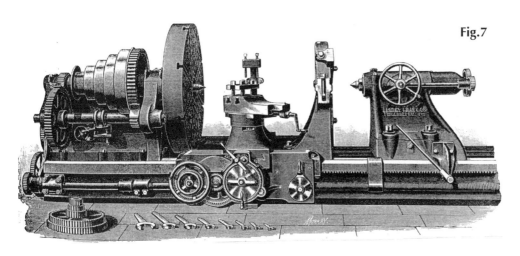

Fig.7

Fig.8

Fig.9

Fig.10

Fig.11

Fig.12

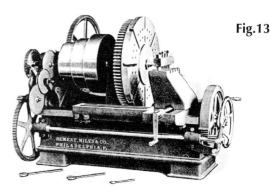

Fig.13

BENSON & RUSSELL, Chicopee Falls, MA

A partnership of J. Benson & Thomas B. Russell. Maker, in 1837, of "turning engines and lathes."

BETTS, E.& A., Wilmington, DE, later
BETTS MACHINE CO., Wilmington, DE

A partnership of Edward T. Betts (1856-1916) and his brother , Alfred Betts, formed in 1861 to make machine tools. The firm continued until 1878 when it was reorganized as the BETTS MACHINE CO., which operated into the 1920s.

Products included 30" screw cutting engine lathes (Fig.1), offered in 1881, and turret head axle lathes (Fig.2), offered in 1888. Lathe production appears to have ceased about 1890 in favor of drilling machines and large boring and turning mills.

Fig.1

30 in. Screw Cutting Lathe.   Weight, with 16 ft. Shears, 10,200 lbs.

Fig.2

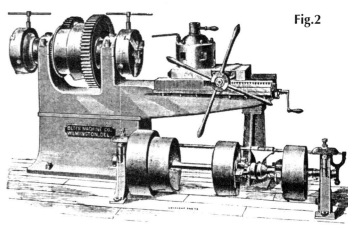

TURRET HEAD AXLE MACHINE.

BIDDEFORD MACHINE SHOP, Biddeford, ME

A large machine shop erected about 1839 as the machinery building arm of the Saco Water Power Co. Primary products were a variety of textile machinery, but the shop also made lathes, planers and shapers c1850-1865.

Sylvanus J. Wetherell served as superintendent 1851-1854, and William H. Thompson from 1854 to 1867. Wetherell was granted a patent for a shaper on March 31, 1857.

BIRKENHEAD, JOHN, Mansfield, MA

A maker of textile spindles beginning about 1864, Birkenhead began making simple 14" engine lathes in 1881 (Fig.1). By 1884 he also offered hand lathes and engine lathes with lead screws and/or back gears. In 1884, he introduced a rotary (turret) tool post (Fig.2) for multiple tooling. Birkenhead retired in 1889, selling all assets to the WINDSOR MACHINE CO.

(Illustrations on the next page.)

Fig.1

J.R.CONANT·BOSTON

NEW ENGINE LATHE.

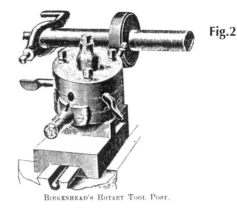

Fig.2

BIRKENHEAD'S ROTARY TOOL POST.

BLAIR, JOSEPH F., Camden, NJ, later
BLAIR & CO., J.F., Camden, NJ

Lathe builder operating 1880-1882. Daniel T. Gage joined as a partner in 1883; the firm became J.F. Blair & Co., which was dissolved in 1886.

BLAISDELL & WOOD, Worcester, MA, later
BLAISDELL & CO., P., Worcester, MA

A partnership of Parritt Blaisdell (?-1875) and Charles Wood, formed in 1865 to make engine lathes, hand lathes, planers and upright drilling machines. Wood left the firm in 1867. It then reorganized as P. BLAISDELL & CO. with John P. Jones as partner, joined in 1873 by Samuel E. Hildreth.

Blaisdell's son, William A., took over when his father died in 1875. By 1882 the firm was the second largest machine tool builder in Worcester, employing 70 to 75 men. William A. Blaisdell operated the firm until 1905, when it was consolidated with the WHITCOMB MFG. CO. to form the WHITCOMB-BLAISDELL MACHINE TOOL CO.

The firm's 1873 catalog offered *NEW PATTERN* lathes in 12" (Fig.1), and 16" swings (Fig.2); as well as improved engine lathes in 18" (Fig.3), 21", 24", and 26" swings (Fig.4). 28" swing engine lathes (Fig.5) were added in 1885.

An improved line of engine lathes was introduced in 1887 and offered in 12" (Fig.6), 14"-16" (Fig.7), 18-22", and 24"-28" (Fig.8) swings. Further improved 24" engine lathes were introduced in 1892.

1904 production included engine lathes with 13" (Fig.9), 15", 16", 17", 18" 19", 20" (Fig.10), 22" 25", 26", 28" and 30" swings. Special 1904 lathes included 17" engine lathes equipped with a taper attachment, and 20" lathes equipped with a quick change feed gear box for use with high speed steel cutting tools (Fig.11).   *(Illustrations continued on next two pages)*

Fig.1

WHITCOMB

Fig.2

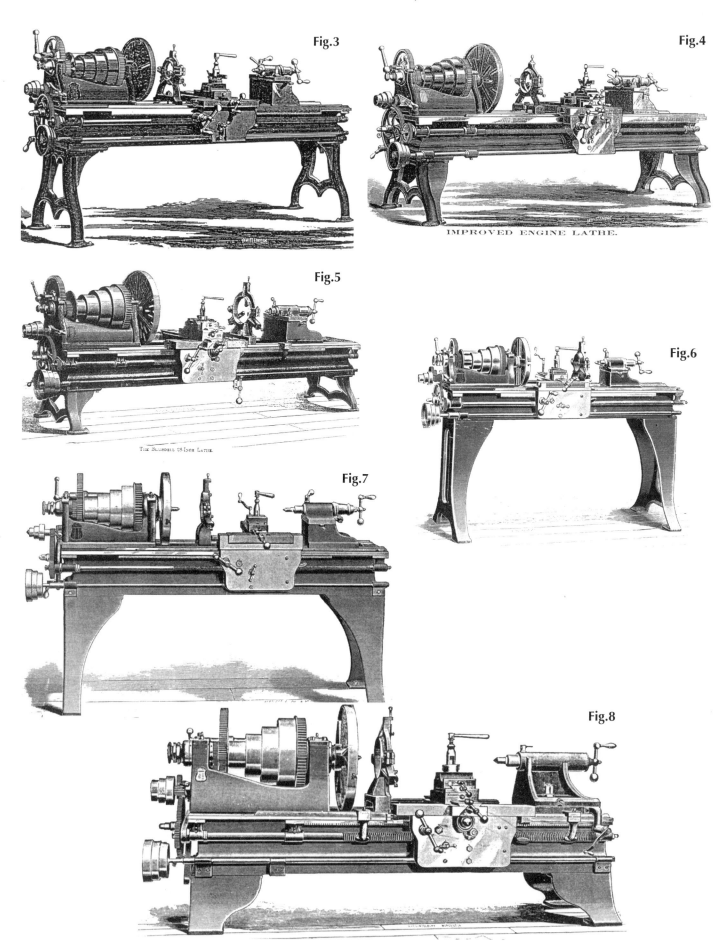

Fig.3

Fig.4

IMPROVED ENGINE LATHE.

Fig.5

THE BLAISDELL 28-INCH LATHE.

Fig.6

Fig.7

Fig.8

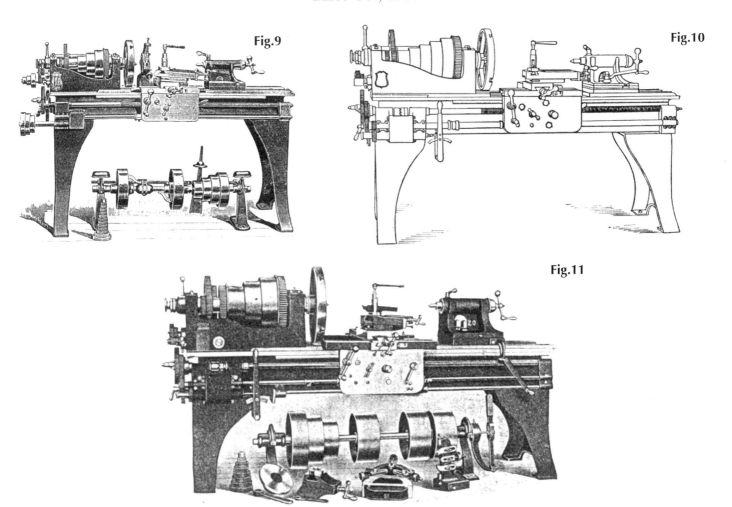

Fig.9

Fig.10

Fig.11

Special High Speed Lathe 20" swing

BLISS CO., E.W., Brooklyn, NY

Founded in 1881 by Eliphalet W. Bliss (1836-1903) to make a line of presses and other metal forming machinery. For a few years, beginning in 1881 and through about 1890, Bliss also offered other machine tools, including 20" engine lathes (Fig.1) and 34" engine lathes (Fig.2). *(Illustrations continued on next page.)*

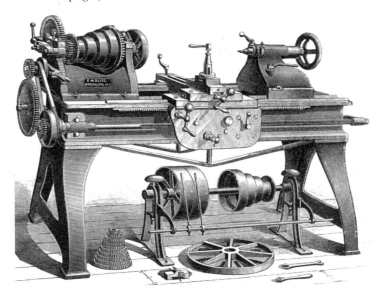

Fig.1

Fig.2

BLOUNT CO., J.G., Everett, MA

    Founded in 1891 by John G. Blount (1858-1943), who served as president until his death, and his brother Eugene I. Blount (1854-1932) who served as treasurer. Primary products were buffing and grinding machines, production of which continued until after World War II.

    Lathe production began in 1902 with the introduction of speed lathes (Fig.1) in 11", 13" and 16" swings. A set-over swivel tailstock option (Fig.2) was introduced in 1903. Slide rest (Fig.3) and turret (Fig.4) attachments were offered by 1910, as were motor driven machines (Fig.5). *(Illustrations continued on next page)*

Fig.1   Fig.2

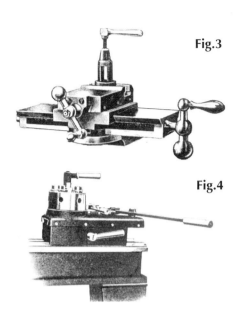

Fig.3

Fig.4

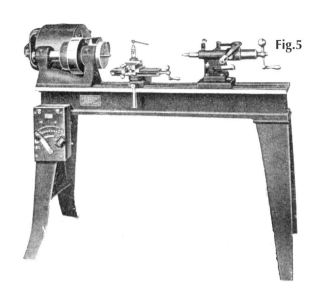

Fig.5

BOGERT, JOHN L., Flushing, L.I., NY

Bogert, who had been a partner in GRANT & BOGERT, began operating under his own name in 1884 when the partnership was dissolved. He remained active until at least 1906.

Products included a long-bed, 21" engine lathe introduced in 1890 (Fig.1). The BOGERT 20" turret engine lathe was introduced in 1893 and offered in three styles; an engine lathe with a turret mounted on the cross slide (Fig.2), a chucking model with a turret mounted on the cross slide (Fig.3), and an engine lathe with a turret mounted on a compound slide. In 1906, Bogert introduced a newly patented crankshaft lathe (Fig.4) which drove the workpiece from both ends to prevent distortion. *(Illustrations continued on next page)*

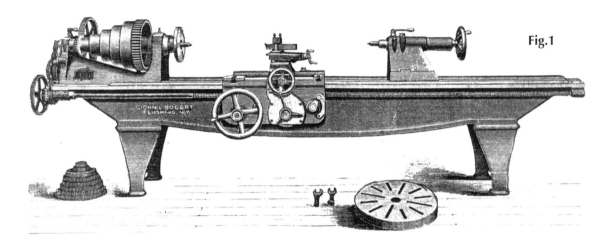

Fig.1

Fig.2

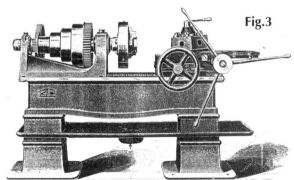

Fig.3

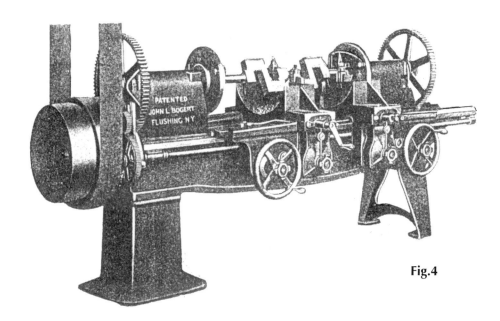

Fig.4

BRADFORD MILL CO., Cincinnati, OH, later
BRADFORD MACHINE TOOL CO., Cincinnati, OH

Founded in 1840 by James Bradford to make flour mill machinery. The firm became the BRADFORD MILL CO. in 1875. In January, 1900, the company sold the flour machinery business and reorganized as the BRADFORD MACHINE TOOL CO., with capital of $100,000 and George F. Stewart as president. Operations continued as late as 1937.

Lathe production began in 1890 when Edward A. Muller, who had been operating as the MULLER MACHINE TOOL CO. in space rented inside the Bradford Mill Co. factory, merged into Bradford. By mid-1891 Bradford was making 30 lathes per month.

MULLER 24" engine lathes (Fig.1), with a feed mechanism patented February 18, 1890, by Edward A. Muller, were introduced in 1891. The line expanded in 1892 to include 18" (Fig.2), 21", 30" (Fig.3), and 36" engine lathes. Muller's short-lived association ended when he moved on to LODGE & DAVIS in 1892.

An improved line of BRADFORD engine lathes in 14", 18" (Fig.4), 21", 24" (Fig.5) and 36" swings was introduced by 1898. In 1901, the 14" size (Fig.6) was available with a new feed gear design called the Universal Feeding and Screw-Cutting Attachment.

Triple geared, 36" and 42" engine lathes for use with high-speed steel tooling were introduced in 1904. Engine lathes with quick change feed gear boxes (Fig.7) were introduced in 1905. *(Illustrations continued on next page)*

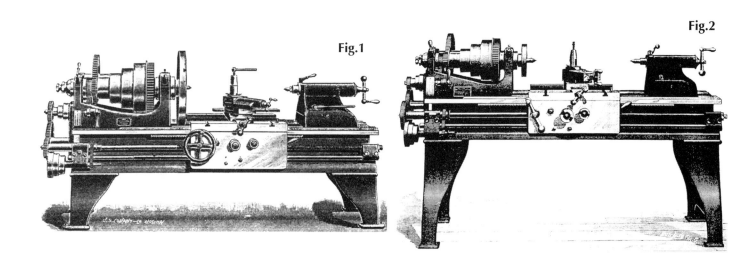

Fig.1

Fig.2

Fig.3

THIRTY-INCH "MULLER" LATHE.

Fig.4

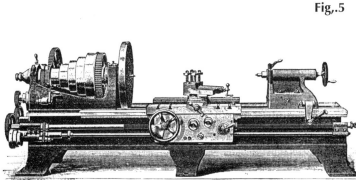

Fig,.5

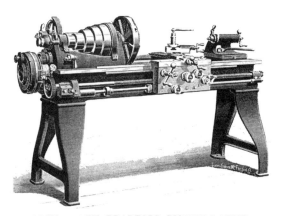

Fig.6

14 IN. x 6 FT. BRADFORD ENGINE LATHE
With Universal Feeding and Screw-Cutting Attachment.

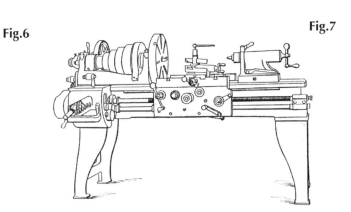

Fig.7

BRIDGEFORD MACHINE TOOL WORKS, Rochester, NY

Founded about 1900 by Charles Bridgeford (?-1914) who had been associated with the GLEASON WORKS. The firm is listed as a lathe builder in 1905 but no details on early lathe types are given. By 1913 lathe production was entirely large, heavy-duty types. In 1919, Bridgeford was absorbed by the BETTS MACHINE CO.

BRIDGEPORT MACHINE TOOL WORKS, Bridgeport, CT

Founded by Edward P. Bullard (1841-1906) on August 20, 1880. Bullard, who had operated a series of machinery sales companies beginning in 1864, also continued to operate E.P. BULLARD CO. as a sales operation. In 1894, Bullard incorporated the BRIDGEPORT MACHINE TOOL WORKS as the BULLARD MACHINE TOOL CO., which continued in business until very recent times.

Lathe production included 16" engine lathes introduced in 1880, 21" engine lathes (Fig.1) equipped with the *LIPE* tool post (Fig.2) introduced in 1883, turret head chucking lathes introduced in 1884 (Fig.3), and 16" *FOX* monitor lathes introduced in 1885 (Fig.4). 37" chucking lathes (Fig.5) were introduced in 1890. 1892 offerings included 20" turret lathes (Fig.6), simple chucking lathes (Fig.7), and extension bed gap lathes (Fig.8). *(Illustrations continued on next page)*

Fig.1

Fig.2

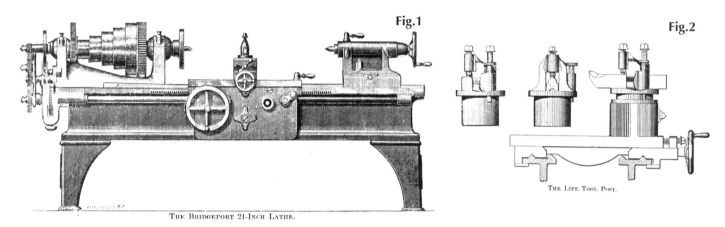

THE BRIDGEPORT 21-INCH LATHE.

THE LIPE TOOL POST.

Fig.3

Fig.4

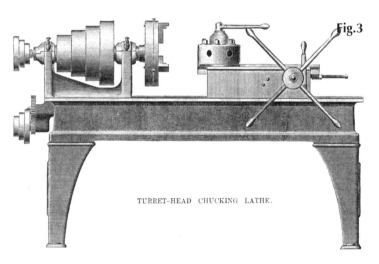

TURRET-HEAD CHUCKING LATHE.

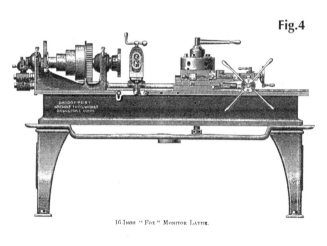

16-INCH "FOX" MONITOR LATHE.

Fig.5

Fig.6

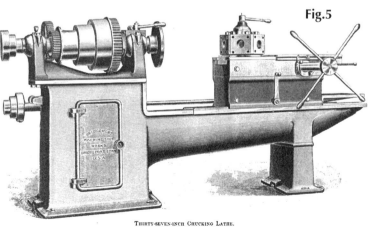

THIRTY-SEVEN-INCH CHUCKING LATHE.

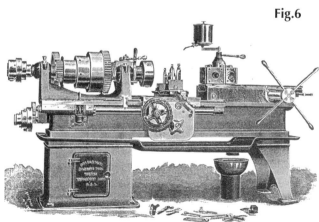

Fig.7 **Fig.8**

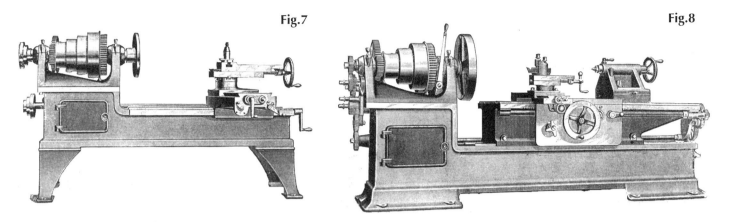

BROWN, JAMES S., Pawtucket, RI

Working for Pitcher & Gay beginning in 1819, Brown developed an improvement in slide rests which, for the first time, allowed adjustment of tool height while the lathe was running. Brown replaced Gay as partner in 1824 and the firm became Pitcher & Brown. In 1842, he bought out Pitcher and began operating under his own name, making lathes, boring machines and gear cutting machines. The business continued until about 1870.

BROWN & SHARPE, J.R., Providence, RI, later
BROWN & SHARPE MFG. CO., Providence, RI

A partnership of Joseph R. Brown (1810-1876) and his former apprentice Lucian Sharpe (1830-1899) formed March 1, 1853. Early products included measuring tools, clocks and sewing machines. Machine tool production began in 1861 when Brown designed a screw machine for firearms makers (Fig.1).

On January 1, 1868, the firm reorganized as the BROWN & SHARPE MFG. CO. and continues under that name today. In 1872 the firm employed 300 workmen. By 1900 employment had grown to 2000 and factory floor space to seven acres. Machine tool production ceased in 1991.

By 1867, screw machines were offered in No.1, 1¼" bar size, (Fig.2); No.3, 5/8" bar size (Fig.3); and No.4, 7/16" bar size (Fig.4). The No.4 screw machine was equipped with a wire feed, patented November 28, 1865. The 9" Universal hand lathe (Fig.5) was introduced in 1880. 1884 production included the above plus an improved model of the No.4 screw machine (Fig.6) and a 16" screw cutting engine lathe (Fig.7).

17" chucking lathes (Fig.8) and new No.5, 1 9/32" bar size, screw machines (Fig.9) were introduced in 1889. The No.6, 1 9/16" bar size, plain screw machine (Fig.10) was introduced in 1891 and a new 13" engine lathe (Fig.11) in 1892.

1902 production included wire feed screw machines in No.1, 1/2 bar size (Fig.12) and No.2, 7/8" bar size, (Fig.13); plain screw machines in No.3, 21/32" bar size (Fig.14) and No.4, 1 9/32" bar size. *(continued next three pages)*

Fig.2

G UN MACHINERY.—SCREW MACHINES, WITH
self-revolving tool heads, suitable for all gun screws and cones.
Tapping machines for lock plates, &c. Address J. R. BROWN &
SHARPE, Providence, R. I.   10 4ª

Fig.1

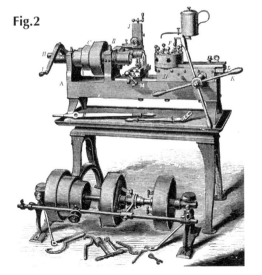

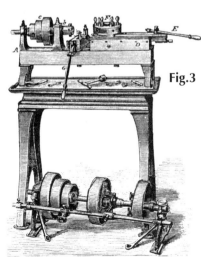

Fig.3

27

Fig.4

UNIVERSAL HAND LATHE.

Fig.5

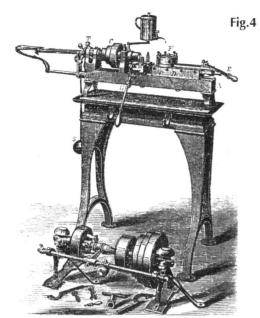

Fig.6

Fig.7

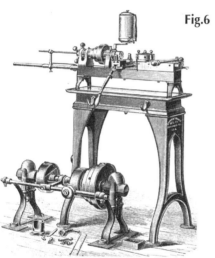

Fig.8

Fig.9

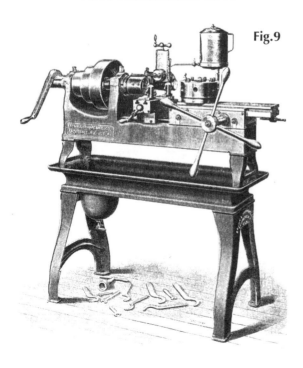

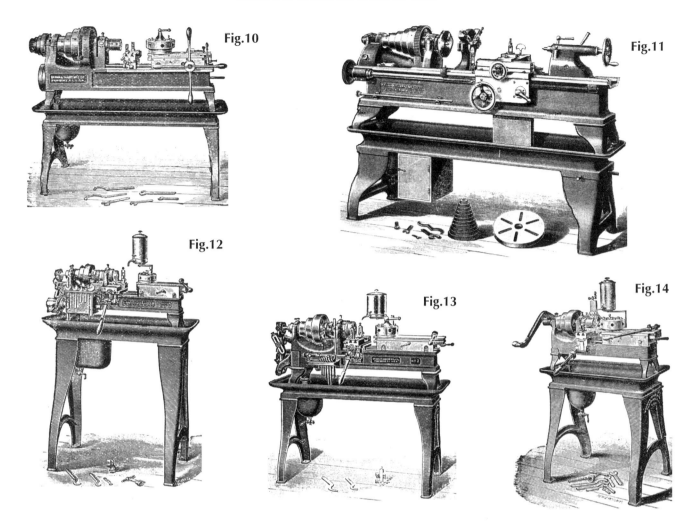

Fig.10

Fig.11

Fig.12

Fig.13

Fig.14

1907 production included No.0, 3/8" bar size (Fig.15), No.1, 5/8" bar size, No.2, 7/8" bar size (Fig.16), No.4, 1 1/4" bar size (Fig.17), and No.6, 1 1/2" bar size (Fig.18) wire feed screw machines. Plain screw machines in No.4, 1 9/32" bar size (Fig.19); No.6, 1 5/8" bar size; and improved horizontal chucking lathes (Fig.20) were also offered in 1907. All except the horizontal chucking lathes were made with improvements patented in 1903 and 1905. *(Illustrations continued on next page.)*

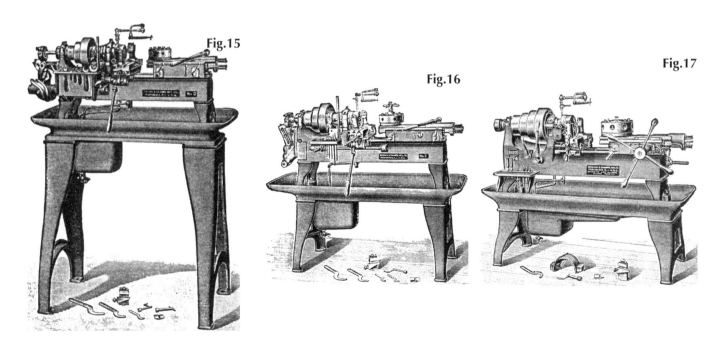

Fig.15

Fig.16

Fig.17

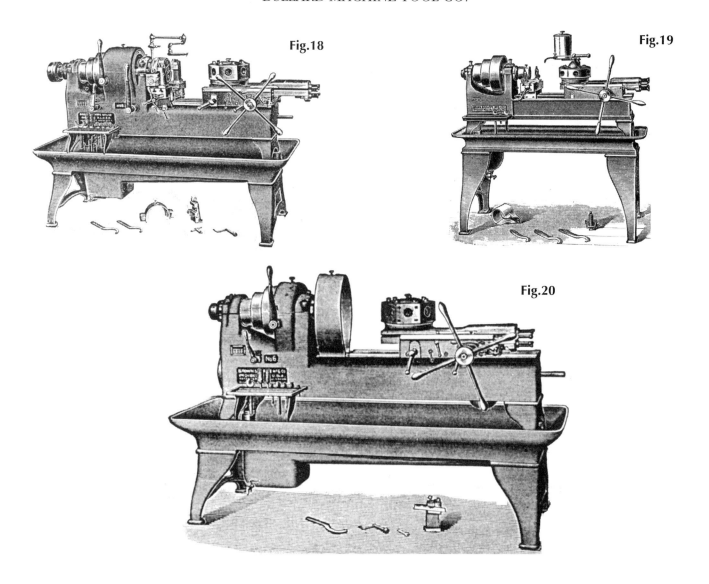

Fig.18

Fig.19

Fig.20

BULLARD MACHINE TOOL CO., Bridgeport, CT

Formed in 1894 as a reorganization of the BRIDGEPORT MACHINE TOOL WORKS. Edward P. Bullard, founder, was president; his sons Edward P. Jr. (1872-1953), Dudley B. (1869-1941), Harold C. (1879-1949), Joseph W.C. (1882-1956), and nephew Agustus H. (1867-1930), filled various executive positions in the firm. Edward P. , Jr. served as president from his father's death in 1906 until 1947.

The firm continued production of the lathes previously made by Bridgeport. By 1897, new offerings included 22" (Fig.1) and 26" (Fig.2) combination turret lathes with the turret mounted on the cross slide, the H model turret lathe (Fig.3), 24" engine lathes (Fig.4), and 26", triple geared engine lathes (Fig.5).

In 1902, the heavy duty 26" *RAPID PRODUCTION* lathe was offered with power traverse for the carriage (Fig.6) and an optional 40 HP electric motor. *(continued on next page)*

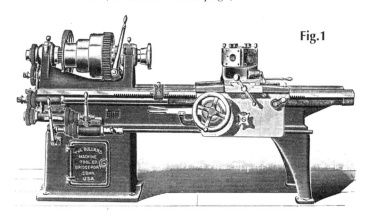

Fig.1

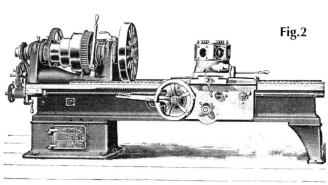

Fig.2

26-INCH COMBINATION TURRET MACHINE.

Fig.3

Engine and turret lathe production appears to have been phased out beginning about 1905. Vertical boring mills and vertical turret lathes became the primary products.

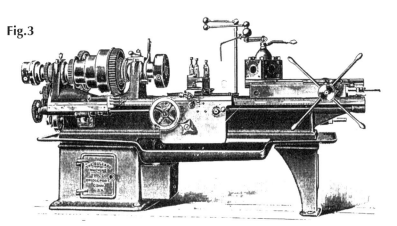

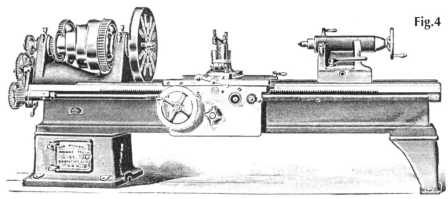

Fig.4

24-INCH LATHE

Fig.5

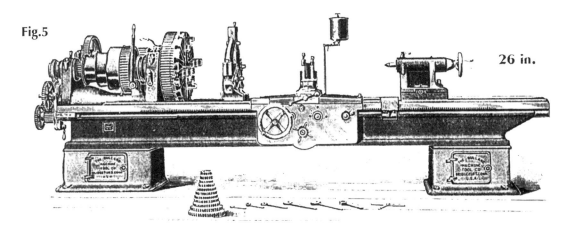

26 in.

Fig.6

BULLOCK, C.K., Philadelphia, PA

Maker, in 1891, of a boring and milling platen designed to be mounted on engine lathes "to enable jobs of boring, facing or milling to be readily done on it which would ordinarily require a boring or milling machine." The platen was offered in two sizes; 12" or 24" square.

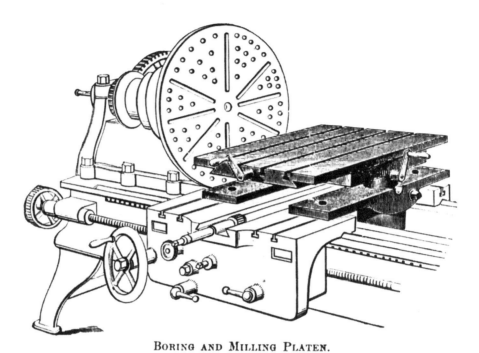

BORING AND MILLING PLATEN.

BURR & SONS, JOHN T., Brooklyn, NY

Founded by John T. Burr (1840-1916) about 1890 to make keyseating machines that he had patented in 1885. Burr operated the company until his death in 1916. The only known lathe product is a small, 12" hand turret lathe introduced in 1897.

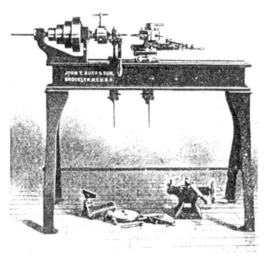

A TURRET HAND LATHE.

CADY, CHARLES L., Lowell, MA

Maker, in 1875, of small lathes, including 8" (Fig.1) and 10" (Fig.2) foot-power lathes with optional slide rests, 12" engine lathes made in foot-power (Fig.3) or countershaft versions, and 18" screw cutting engine lathes with beds from 6' to 10'.

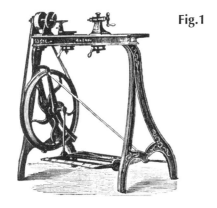

Fig.1

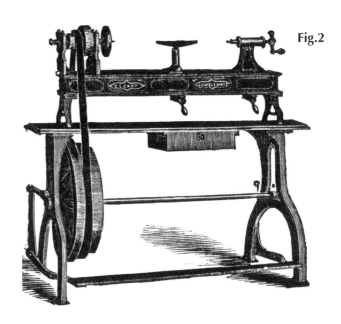

Fig.2

Fig.3

CAIRO IRON & MACHINE WORKS, Cairo, IL, later
CAIRO MACHINE WORKS, Cairo, IL

Founded in 1864 by Joseph B. Reed (1831-1911) to do repair work on the government fleet of river boats during the Civil War. About 1880, Reed and his son Frank began making engine lathes (Fig.1) in 20", 22", 24", 26", 28", and 30" swings. Lathes produced in 1909 (Fig.2) were only slightly improved over the earlier model.

Frank Reed continued to make identical lathes after taking over the firm at his father's death. Lathe production stopped in 1918 but the firm continued in business until 1949.

(Illustrations continued on next page)

Fig.1

REED'S NEW ENGINE LATHE.

33

Fig.2

CARROLL & JAMIESON MACHINE CO., Batavia, OH, later
CARROLL-JAMIESON MACHINE TOOL CO., Batavia, OH

Founded in 1903 by Arthur V. Carroll (1875-1944) and P.F. Jamieson. The firm incorporated in 1904 as the CARROLL-JAMIESON MACHINE TOOL CO. with $10,000 capital and Carroll as president and general manager.

1903 production appears to have been 9" foot-power lathes (Fig.1) only. By 1909, 14" engine lathes with quick change feed gear boxes (Fig.2) were advertised as their sole offering; 15" engine lathes were added 1n 1910.

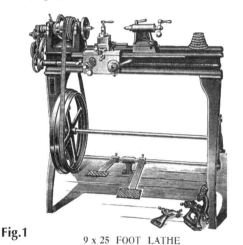

Fig.1

9 x 25 FOOT LATHE

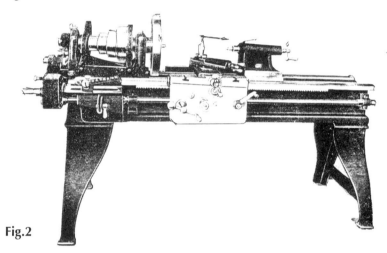

Fig.2

CATARACT TOOL & OPTICAL CO., Buffalo, NY

Formed about 1895 to make small bench lathes and other tools for the optical industry. The firm went into receivership in late 1901 and the lathe line was sold to HARDINGE BROTHERS in 1902.

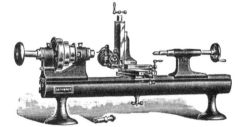

CATARACT PRECISION LATHE WITH MILLING ATTACHMENT.

CHAMBERLIN D., Boston, MA

Maker of lathes and planers in 1853. The business continued until at least 1870.

CHAMPION TOOL WORKS, Cincinnati, OH

Formed in 1905 to make 10" and 12" engine lathes that had previously been made by the R.K. LeBLOND MACHINE TOOL CO. H.W. Kreuzburg, who had been with the BRADFORD MACHINE TOOL CO. was superintendent and co-owner.

Larger, 14" engine lathes (Fig.1) for use with high speed steel tooling were introduced in 1906. 18" engine lathes with quick change gear boxes (Fig.2) or with double back gears were introduced in 1909. *(Illustrations continued on next page)*

Fig.1

Fig.2

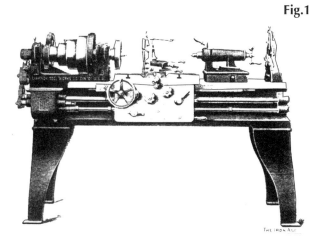

CHAPIN, WILLIAM A., St. Johnsbury, VT

Inventor and maker of an engine lathe with speed changing gears mounted inside the cone pulley, patented October 2, 1849. He appears to have been backed by scale maker E. & T. Fairbanks.

CHICAGO LATHE CO., Chicago, IL

Lathe builder operating in 1882.

CHICAGO MACHINE TOOL CO., Chicago, IL

Formed in 1902, the company appears to have been controlled by HILL, CLARKE & CO., a large Boston machinery dealer that acted as sole agent. Albert W. Wigglesworth, treasurer of Hill, Clarke, served as president until his death in 1917. The firm ceased operation in 1919.

1903 production was limited to hand milling machines and a line of CHICAGO speed lathes in 10", 12" (shown at right), and 16" swings.

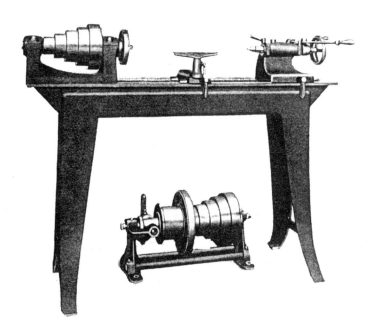

CHICKERING, W.F., Worcester, MA

Maker, in 1903, of 11" swing speed lathes equipped with patent, lever operated tail stocks.

CINCINNATI LATHE & TOOL CO., Cincinnati, OH

Formed in 1906 by William C. Heindel to take over the lathe business of the FOSDICK MACHINE TOOL CO. Heindel served as president until selling the company to the Cincinnati Milling Machine Co. in 1945.

Products included the CINCINNATI 16" engine lathe (Fig.1) with the Emme's patent quick change gear box, offered in 1908, and a 16" engine lathe with an improved feed gear box (Fig.2), introduced in 1909. *(Illustrations on next page)*

THE CINCINNATI SIXTEEN-INCH INSTANTANEOUS
CHANGE GEAR ENGINE LATHE.
WITH W. T. EMMES PATENTED FEED DEVICE AND DOUBLE BACK GEARS.

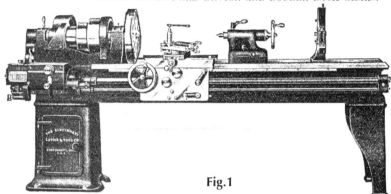

Fig.1

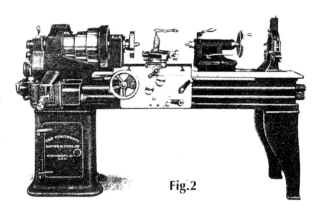

Fig.2

COLUMBIAN IRON FOUNDRY & MACHINE TOOL WORKS, Chicago, IL

Founded 1865 by Charles W. Parker. The firm made a "specialty of building heavy lathes and planers for the various railroads". Parker retired in 1883 and the firm appears to have lasted only a few years afterwards.

CONWAY & CO., M.R., Cincinnati, OH

Maker, beginning in 1883, of a line of engine lathes, including the 20" swing model shown below.

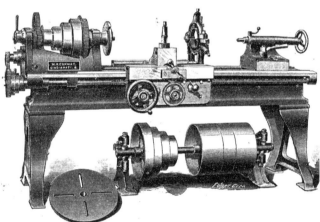

New 20-inch Swing Lathe.—M. R. Conway & Co., Cincinnati, Ohio.

COOMBS & CO., S.C., Worcester, MA

A partnership of Samuel C. Coombs, Russell R. Shepard, and Martin Lathe, formed in 1845. Maker of a variety of machine tools, including engine lathes.

The firm was reorganized as SHEPARD, LATHE & CO. when Coombs left in 1853.

COOPER, JONES & CADBURY, Philadelphia, PA

A partnership of William S. Cooper, Thomas J. Jones, Joel Cadbury and John W. Cadbury, formed about 1875. The firm is listed in 1879 as a maker of brass finishers' lathes.

COULTER & McKENZIE, Bridgeport, CT

A partnership of Thomas Coulter and Hector McKenzie formed in 1876. Coulter, in a 1901 article, claimed that the firm was the builder of the first "large" turret lathe, patented by the partners on February 17, 1874, and December 11, 1876. Coulter's article included the illustration below and described the lathe as having wooden bed and iron legs. Size was not specified, but the work pieces shown are iron wagon axles.

DAVIS & CO., GEORGE W., Nashua, NH, later
DAVIS, GEORGE W. & S.A., Nashua, NH

Formed in 1863 by George W. Davis (1828-1897). The firm supplied machine tools, including lathes, to the Springfield Armory during the Civil War. In 1879, the firm reorganized as GEORGE W. & S.A. DAVIS, which continued to make lathes and other machine tools.

DAVIS & EGAN MACHINE TOOL CO., Cincinnati, OH

A partnership of Charles Davis (1853-1903) and Thomas P. Egan, formed September 1, 1896, as a reorganization of the LODGE & DAVIS MACHINE TOOL CO. The company was reorganized in 1898 as the AMERICAN TOOL WORKS CO. when Davis sold out to Franklin Alter.

Products included an early form of automatic lathe (Fig.1), introduced in 1896, a line of engine lathes from 12" swing to 60" swing (Figs.2-3), and turret lathes/screw machines from ½" bar size (Fig.4) to 1¼" bar size (Fig.5). These machines were often sold in multiples, completely tooled to make specific parts. *(Illustrations continued on next page)*

Fig.1   **Fig.2**

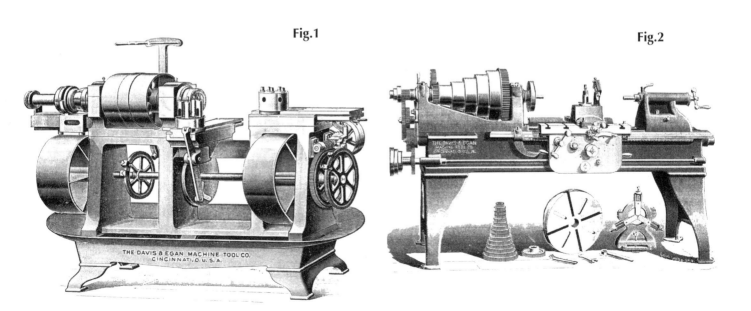

THE LARGEST LINE OF ENGINE LATHES MADE UNDER ONE MANAGEMENT IN THE U. S.

☞ 12", 14", 16", 18", 20", 22", 24", 28", 30", 36", 40", 52" and 60" swing.
☞ Patent Drop V Bed furnished with all Lathes above 20".
☞ Crucible Steel Spindles finished on Universal Grinding Machines.
☞ Patent Automatic Stops to the Carriage.
☞ Power Cross Feed, with Micrometer Adjustment.

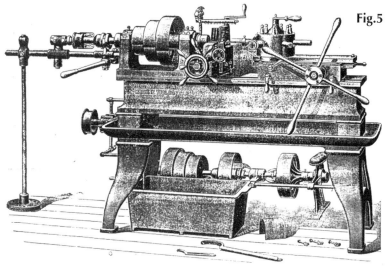

BICYCLE PEDAL BARREL MACHINE

DAVIS, SAMUEL, Worcester, MA

Maker, in 1844, of "turning engines and lathes."

DAVIS, W.P., Rochester, NY, later
DAVIS MACHINE CO., W.P., Rochester, NY

Founded in 1887 by William P. Davis (1850-1910) to make his patented key seater. Davis operated both as a machinery dealer and a machine tool maker. Early lathe production included 26" heavy speed lathes (Fig.1) introduced in 1889 and 8" foot lathes (Fig.2) in 1892.

In 1894, Davis, joined by his brother Charles F. Davis (1861-1932), reorganized as the DAVIS MACHINE TOOL CO., which offered a much wider selection of lathes. William P. Davis died in 1910; Charles F. Davis left the firm in 1914. The new owners reorganized in 1915 as the DAVIS MACHINE TOOL CO.

Products in 1897 included stud lathes (Fig.3), 14" engine lathes (Fig.4), 16" engine lathes (Fig.5) and 18" engine lathes.

Davis' 1905 catalog offered an improved line of lathes, including 10" foot power lathes (Fig.6) and light duty 10" and 12" (Fig.7) engine lathes. Standard duty engine lathes were offered in 14" (Fig.8), 16", 18" (Fig.9), 22", 26", 28" and 32" (Fig.10) sizes. Heavy duty,

38

triple geared engine lathes were available in 36" and 42" swings (Fig.11). Turret head chucking lathes were available in 18" and 22" models (Fig.12).

A 16" engine lathe with quick change feed gear box and a rather awkwardly mounted motor drive (Fig.13) were introduced in 1909. *(Illustrations continued on next two pages)*

Fig.1

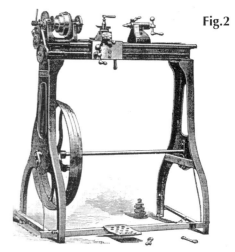

Fig.2

8 INCH SCREW CUTTING LATHE.

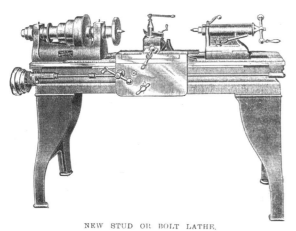

Fig.3

NEW STUD OR BOLT LATHE.

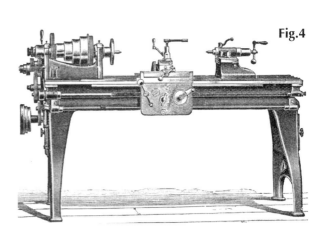

Fig.4

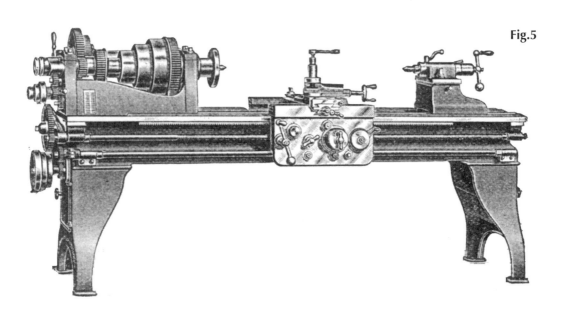

Fig.5

Fig.6

Fig.7

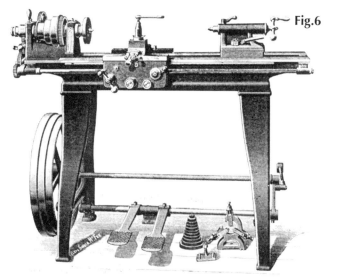

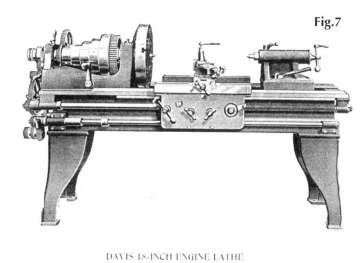

DAVIS 18=INCH ENGINE LATHE

DAVIS 10=INCH FOOT POWER SCREW CUTTING ENGINE LATHE

Fig.8

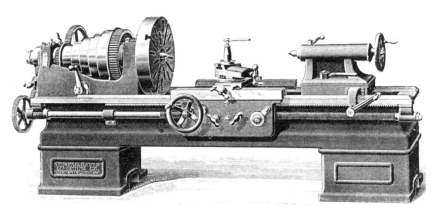

DAVIS 28=INCH ENGINE LATHE

Fig.9

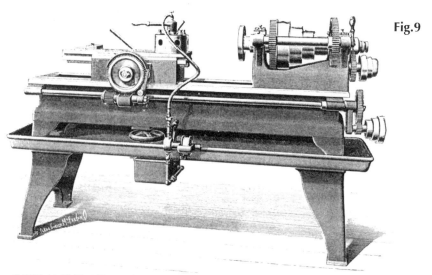

DAVIS 18=INCH AND 22=INCH TURRET HEAD CHUCKING LATHE =(Gears Cased)

Fig.10

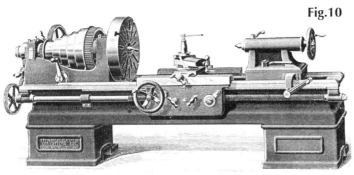

DAVIS 28-INCH ENGINE LATHE

Fig.11

DAVIS 42-INCH TRIPLE GRAND ENGINE LATHE

Fig.12

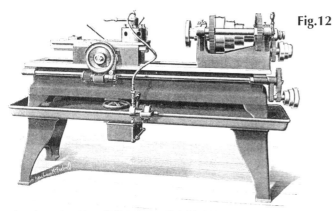

DAVIS 18-INCH AND 22-INCH TURRET HEAD CHUCKING LATHE – (Gears Cased)

Fig.13

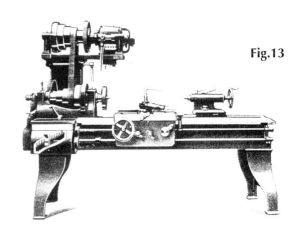

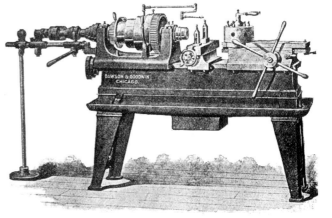

SCREW MACHINE.

DAWSON & GOODWIN, Chicago, IL

A partnership including John H. Dawson, formed about 1895 to make a line of turret lathes/screw machines such as those shown below. The firm was dissolved in 1901. *(Illustration at right)*

DELANO, E.A., Chicago, IL

Maker, c1885, of pulley turning lathes "made under his recent patents."

DEXTER MACHINE CO., Dexter, ME, later
DEXTER TOOL CO., Dexter, ME

Formed in 1887 as successor to the DUSTIN MFG. CO. Products included the lines of engine lathes and drilling machines previously made by Dustin.

In 1892 the firm reorganized as the DEXTER TOOL CO. with capital of $10,000 and twenty employees. S.S. Ireland was president and Norman H. Fay, of FAY & SCOTT, treasurer, indicating that the company was controlled by FAY & SCOTT, also of Dexter, ME.

In 1895, the reorganized company offered 10" and 12" speed lathes, and 16", 18" *(illustrated next page)*, 21", 24", 28" and 32" screw-cutting engine lathes. The engine lathes were priced from $250 for the 16" up to $800 for the 32" size and were "guaranteed first-class." *(Illustration on next page)*

DIETZ MACHINE TOOL CO.,   Cincinnati, OH

Formed in 1899 with capital of $25,000. Incorporators were Jacob Dietz, William Lodge, Murray Shipley and Louis J. Dolle. Dietz had previously been a partner in DIETZ, SCHUMACHER & BOYE.

The firm operated as a captive manufacturer of lathes that were sold by LODGE & SHIPLEY CO. and probably never made machines for sale under its own name.

DIETZ, GANG & CO.,   Cincinnati, OH, later
DIETZ, SCHUMACHER & CO.,   Cincinnati, OH, later
DIETZ, SCHUMACHER & BOYE,   Cincinnati, OH

Originally a partnership of Jacob Dietz (1849-1926) and William E. Gang (1855-1932) formed in 1888 to make radial drills and engine lathes in 14" (Fig.1) and 22" (Fig.2) sizes. Dietz had previously operated as J. DIETZ & CO.; Gang had been general manager of LODGE, DAVIS & CO.

The firm reorganized as DIETZ, SCHUMACHER & CO. when Gang left in 1893 and was replaced by Ernst A. Schumacher, who had previously operated as E.A. SCHUMACHER & CO. The lathe line was expanded to include 16" (Fig.3), 24" and 26" (Fig.4) models.

On April, 1, 1896, Frederick W. Boye, Jr. was admitted as a partner. The firm reorganized as DIETZ, SCHUMACHER & BOYE and continued to offer the same products in an expanded factory. Dietz left the firm in 1899 to form the DIETZ MACHINE TOOL CO. The remaining partners then reorganized as SCHUMACHER & BOYE. *(Illustrations continued on next page)*

Fig.1

Fig.2

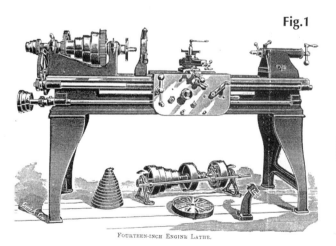

FOURTEEN-INCH ENGINE LATHE.

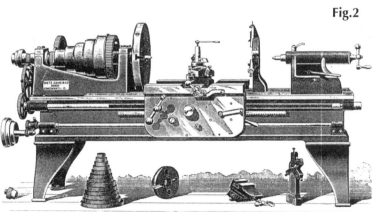

TWENTY-TWO-INCH ENGINE LATHE.

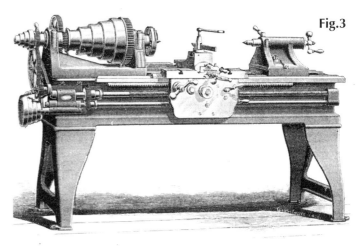

Fig.3

NEW SIXTEEN-INCH ENGINE LATHE.

Fig.4

TWENTY-SIX-INCH ENGINE LATHE.

DONALDSON, WILLIAM, Cincinnati, OH

Maker, beginning about 1872, of *ACME* 7" foot power engine lathes. He closed this business in 1878 to join LODGE & DAVIS.

DRAPER MACHINE TOOL CO., Worcester, MA

Formed in 1892 when William F. Draper (1842-1910), owner of a large loom-making firm, bought the assets of the defunct LATHE & MORSE TOOL CO. Production of hand lathes and engine lathes continued, based on Lathe & Morse designs and, in 1893, included 15" engine lathes (Fig.1) and 32" to 36" engine lathes (Fig.2).

1903 production included engine lathes from 20" (Fig.3) to 38" (Fig.4) sizes, newly introduced 24" turret lathes (Fig.5) and 16" taper turning lathes (Fig.6) with the head and tail stocks mounted on a swivel plate. In 1904, an apron mounted, quick feed change gear box was introduced (Fig.7). The firm was absorbed into the WHITCOMB-BLAISDELL MACHINE TOOL CO. in 1905. *(Illustrations continued on next page)*

Fig.1

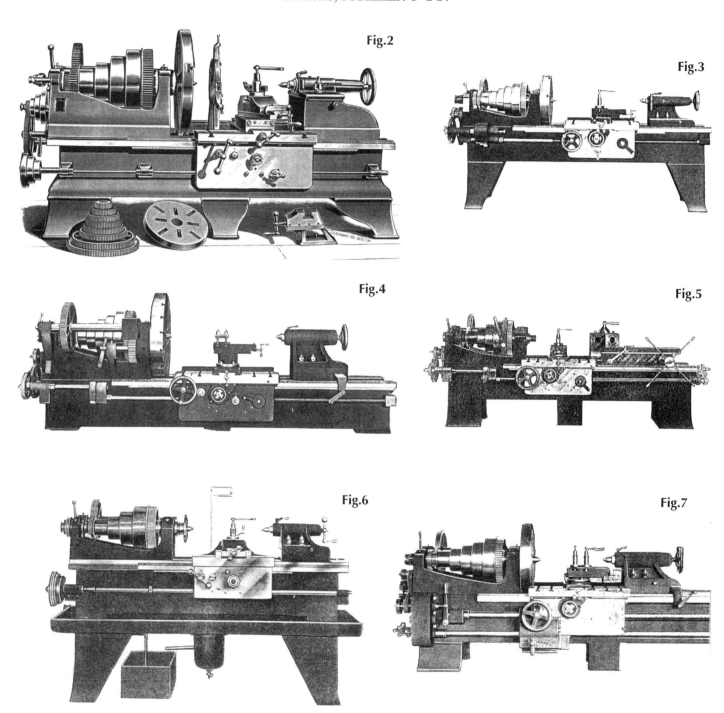

Fig.2

Fig.3

Fig.4

Fig.5

Fig.6

Fig.7

DRESES, MUELLER & CO., Cincinnati, OH, later,
DRESES MACHINE TOOL CO., Cincinnati, OH

Formed in late 1895 by Henry Dreses (1854-1930), Oscar W. Mueller (1863-1936), William Gilbert and Charles Lange. Fifty hands were employed. Dreses had been chief engineer of LODGE, DAVIS & CO. Mueller, who had also been associated with LODGE, DAVIS & CO., sold out in 1902 and formed the MUELLER MACHINE TOOL CO. Dreses then reorganized as the DRESES MACHINE TOOL CO., which operated until 1939.

Early products included light turret lathes and brassworkers' lathes (Fig.1). 1908 production included 18" universal monitor lathes (Fig.2), and 16" set over turret lathes (Fig.3). A 13" brassworkers' turret lathe equipped with an electric motor driving through double cone pulleys (Fig.4) was introduced in 1909. *(Illustrations continued on next page)*

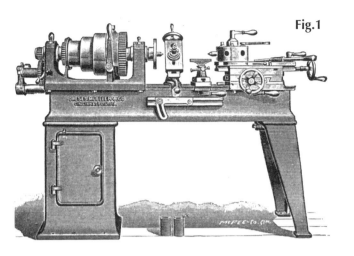

Fig.1

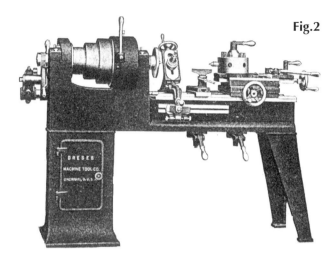

Fig.2

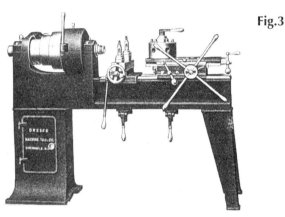

Fig.3

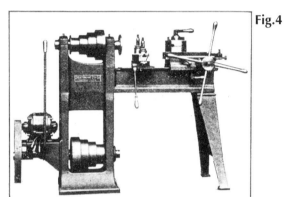

Fig.4

DUSTIN MFG. CO., Dexter, ME

Operated by N. Dustin & Co., the firm made 26" engine lathes and 20" upright drills beginning prior to 1884. In 1887, the DEXTER MACHINE CO. was formed to take over the factory and assets.

DUVINGE, LEWIS, New York, NY

Maker, in 1868, of shapers and engine lathes.

EDDY, W.H., Worcester, MA, later
EDDY CO. WILLIAM H., Worcester, MA

Founded in 1873 by William H. Eddy (1831-1903) to make twist drill grinders, lathes and planers. Eddy sold out in 1900 to parties who reorganized as the WILLIAM H. EDDY CO.

Production in the 1890s was marketed through Hill, Clarke & Co. which offered the machines under the Hill, Clarke name. Lathe offerings included 22" (Fig.1) and 40" (Fig.2) turret chucking lathes.

By 1901 production was sold under the Eddy name and included 22" and 24" turret lathes (Fig.3). Similar lathes were offered up to 50" in size. *(Illustrations continued on next page)*

Eddy Turret Head Chucking Lathe, 22 Inch Swing.

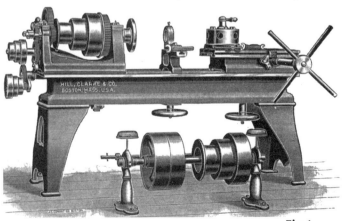

Fig.1

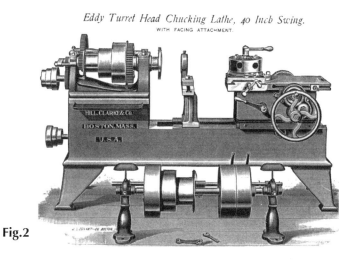

Eddy Turret Head Chucking Lathe, 40 Inch Swing.
WITH FACING ATTACHMENT.

Fig.2

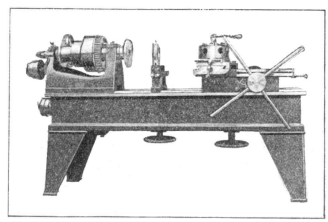

Fig.3

EDWARDS & CO., T.M., Keene, NH
Maker of a large engine lathe for the Harpers Ferry Armory in 1839.

ELGIN TOOL WORKS, Elgin, IL
Formed by Albert A. Hasselquist (1863-1939) in 1904 as a reorganization of A. HASSELQUIST & CO. The firm continued to make a line of small bench lathes for the watchmaking industry. A typical 1909 bench lathe, complete with countershaft and milling attachment, is shown below.

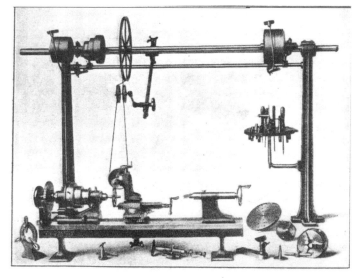

ENGINEERING APPLIANCE CO., Jamestown, NY
Maker, in 1895, of light bench lathes "for bicycle, watch work, or tool room."

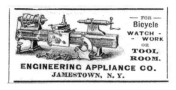

ERMENTROUT, W.H., Reading, PA
Maker, in 1893, of 12" tool room lathes with "automatic cross feed and independent screw for threading."

EUGENE IRON WORKS, Eugene, OR
Operated by G.N. Frazer, proprietor, who began about 1880. A 1908 article states that the firm was "the only one on the Pacific slope that builds lathes for sale." *(continued on next page)*

Products in 1908 included 30" engine lathes like that shown below. Earlier production included engine lathes with up to 44" swing.

EXETER MACHINE WORKS, Exeter, NH

Operated by William H. Burlingame. Maker, c1867-1901, of light engine lathes, hand lathes, and brassworkers' lathes, including foot lathes. Worcester R. Warner and Ambrose Swasey served apprenticeships here before going on to the PRATT & WHITNEY CO. and later forming WARNER & SWASEY.

FAIRBANKS, GEORGE L., Worcester, MA

Lathe maker c1881-1888. Products included bench lathes (Fig.1) offered in 1881 and 11" hand lathes (Fig.2) offered in 1886. Fairbanks was active as late as 1901 when he was granted a lathe patent.

NEW BENCH LATHE.   **Fig.1**

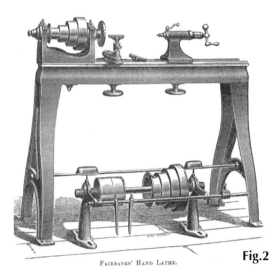

FAIRBANKS' HAND LATHE.   **Fig.2**

FAIRBANKS MACHINE TOOL CO., Springfield, OH, later
FAIRBANKS CO., Springfield, OH

Formed in 1898 to make lathes, the firm was owned by the Springfield Foundry Co. In 1903 the firm consolidated with the Springfield Foundry Co. and the U.S. Tool Holder Co. to form the FAIRBANKS CO. M.L. Milligan was president and N.H. Fairbanks vice president and treasurer. The new firm continued lathe production for several years, but tool holders became the primary product.

FALKENAU, A., Philadelphia, PA

Formed in 1891 by Arthur Falkenau. Early products included tool grinders, traveling cranes and 14" engine lathes such as that shown below. Lathe production appears to have ceased by 1900.

The business continued until 1902 when Falkenau merged with the Philadelphia Machine Tool Co. and reorganized as the FALKENAU-SINCLAIR MACHINE CO. *(Illustration on next page)*

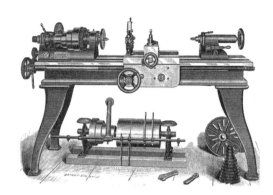

Falkenau

FANEUIL WATCH TOOL CO.,   Boston, MA

Founded in 1884 by Edward Rivett (1851-1937) to make small bench lathes for the watch industry. The firm was reorganized as the RIVETT LATHE MFG. CO. about 1905.

Rivett's first lathe was the No.3 bench lathe offered with a great variety of attachments (Fig.1), including one for gear cutting and milling (Fig.2) and as a turret model (Fig.3). The larger, 8" No.4, was introduced in 1890 (Fig.4) and was also offered with many attachments, including a slotting attachment (Fig.5).

Fig.1

Fig.2

Fig.3

Fig.4

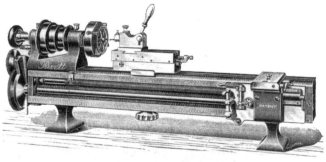

THE RIVETT EIGHT-INCH PRECISION LATHE WITH SLOTTING ATTACHMENT.

Fig.5

FAY, L.D., Worcester, MA
Maker of engine lathes and FAY'S combined engine lathe and milling machine, beginning in 1864 and continuing until 1869 or later.

FAY'S COMBINED SCREW LATHE AND MILLING MACHINE.

FAY & SCOTT, Dexter, ME
A partnership of Norman H. Fay (1852-1919) and Walter Scott, formed in 1881 to make lathes and woodworking machinery. It was best known for its patternmakers' lathes. Fay bought out Scott in 1896 and became president when the firm incorporated in 1901.

Early products included 10", 12" and 16" speed lathes (Fig.1) introduced in 1882, and 10" bench lathes (Fig.2) introduced in 1883. Later production included 24" (Fig.3) and 66" (Fig.4) patternmakers' lathes introduced in 1892. 28" and 32" engine lathes (Fig.5) offered in 1893 were probably made by the DEXTER TOOL CO., a maker of engine lathes formed in 1892 and controlled by FAY & SCOTT.

20" universal turret lathes (Fig.6), introduced in 1899, were sold only through the PRENTISS TOOL & SUPPLY CO., probably under the Prentiss name. 28"-52" extension bed gap lathes (Fig.7) were introduced in 1905. *(Illustrations continued on next page)*

Fig.1

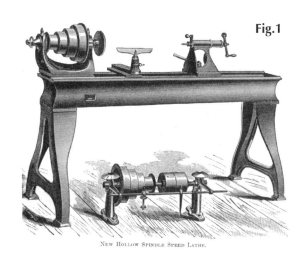

NEW HOLLOW SPINDLE SPEED LATHE.

Fig.2

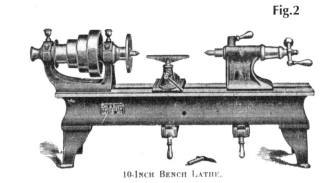

10-INCH BENCH LATHE.

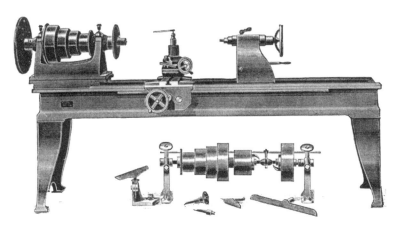

Fig.3

Fig.4

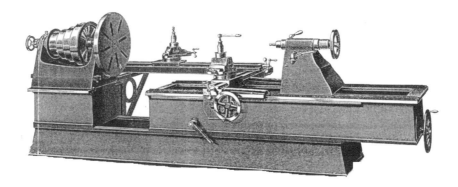

SIXTY-SIX-INCH PATTERN MAKERS' LATHE.

Fig.5

Fig.6

Fig.7

FENN-SADLER MACHINE CO.,   Hartford, CT

A partnership of Wilson L. Fenn (1858-1921) and Joseph F. Sadler formed in 1900 when Fenn left the Woodward & Rogers Co. The firm reorganized as the Fenn Mfg. Co. when Sadler left in 1905. Products included multiple spindle drilling machines and small, 7" swing bench lathes *(right)*.

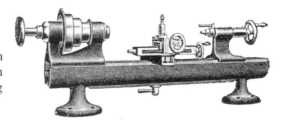

FERRIS & MILES,   Philadelphia, PA

A partnership of Oscar C. Ferris and Frederick B. Miles formed about 1870. The partners sold out to James Dougherty in 1880; he reorganized the firm as the MACHINE TOOL WORKS.

Products included the engine lathe shown next page. Note the quick change feed gear arrangement patented by Miles on February 14, 1871.

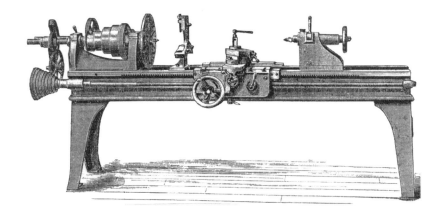

Ferris & Miles

FIFIELD, GEO. W., Lowell, MA, later
FIFIELD TOOL CO., Lowell, MA

Founded in 1873 by George W. Fifield (1848-1911). By 1879 he was offering engine lathes from 16" to 48" swing (Fig.1). An improved version with 30", 38" and 50" swings was available by 1893 (Fig.2).

In 1894, the firm reorganized as the FIFIELD TOOL CO.. which continued to make engine lathes (Fig.3) until the factory burned in 1901.

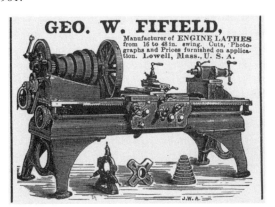

Fig.1

Fig.2

Fig.3

FINNEY & RHODES, Hartford, CT

A partnership of Richard L. Finney and L.E. Rhodes formed in 1892 to make a 14" lathe (Fig. 1) with a shaper attachment (Fig.2). This is the only such combination known. Finney left the firm in 1897 and Rhodes reorganized as L.E. RHODES & CO.

(Illustrations on next page)

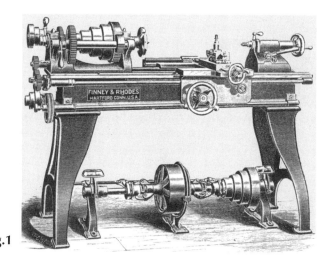

Fig.1

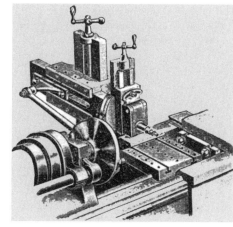

Fig.2

Finney & Rhodes

FISCHER FOUNDRY & MACHINE CO.,   Pittsburgh, PA

Founded by William Fischer (1822-1895) about 1859 to make a variety of machinery for steel mills. In 1891, Fischer introduced a line of roll lathes that utilized a worm drive to get the high reduction ratio desirable when turning heavy rolls. The machine was offered in five sizes to turn 8", 12", 18", 24" and 36" rolls.

New Worm-Driven Roll Lathe

FISH MACHINE WORKS, H.C., Worcester, MA

Formed in 1889 by Henry C. Fish (1825-1906) who had been associated with the L.W. POND MACHINE CO. In 1896 the company announced that it was the maker of the 14" FISH engine lathe formerly known as the PRENTISS lathe. Prentiss was a large machinery dealer for which Fish had been making private label machines.

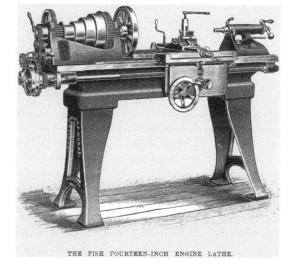

THE FISH FOURTEEN-INCH ENGINE LATHE.

FITCHBURG MACHINE CO., Fitchburg, MA, later
FITCHBURG MACHINE WORKS, Fitchburg, MA

Formed January 1, 1867, as a stock company reorganization of S.C. WRIGHT & CO. Sylvester C. Wright (1816-1880) was superintendent and his son-in-law, James L. Chapman (?-1914) was secretary. In 1877, the company was reorganized as the FITCHBURG MACHINE WORKS.

Marcus A. Coolidge (1865-1947) bought the company in 1905 and, in 1924, merged it with the SENECA FALLS MFG. CO. to form the Seneca Falls Machine Co. Products included 18" engine lathes offered in 1867 (Fig.1). The 1871 catalog offered 12" (Fig.2), 16", 18" (Fig.3), 21", and 24" (Fig.4) engine lathes. By 1874 a line of large engine lathes with swings of 28" to 60" was offered. These large lathes were equipped with S.C. Wright's patent friction and inside power cross feed and were priced from $1,081 for the 28" model to $3,540 for the 60". The 38" model is shown in Fig.5. An axle lathe (Fig.6), which could swing 8'2" between centers, was also offered in 1874.

Later production included extension bed gap lathes (Fig.7), introduced in 1890. 1895 offerings included 20" (Fig.8), 24", and 60" (Fig.9) engine lathes. A 27/50" patternmakers' gap lathe (Fig.10) was introduced in 1896 and the 14" swing GEM lathe (Fig.11) in 1897. By 1900 Fitchburg offered an improved line of engine lathes from 14" to 60" (Figs.12-13).

The well-known *LO-SWING* lathe (Fig.14), designed by James Hartness, was introduced in 1905. An improved model, with two large carriages instead of four smaller carriages, was introduced in 1907. *(continued on next two pages)*

Fig.1

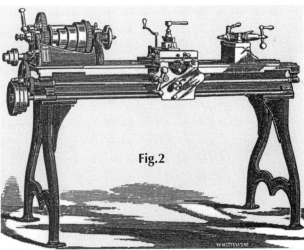

Fig.2

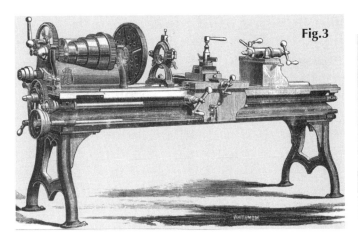

Fig.3

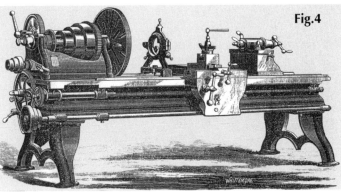

Fig.4

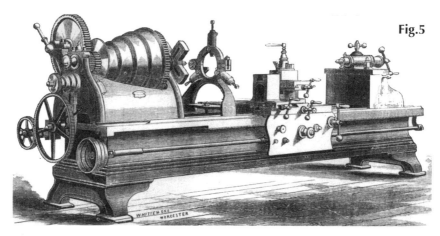

Fig.5

Fig.6

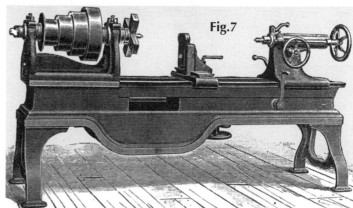

Fig.7

Fig.8

Fig.9

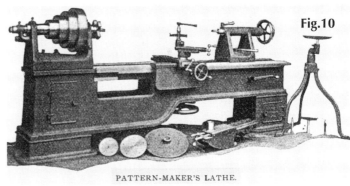

Fig.10

PATTERN-MAKER'S LATHE.

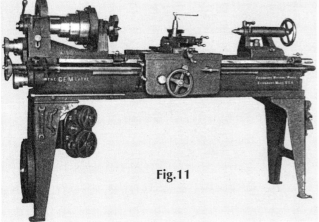

Fig.11

Fig.12

Fig.13

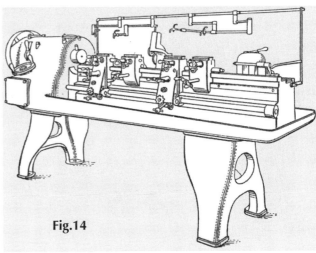

Fig.14

FLAGG, S.H.,   Worcester, MA, later
FLAGG & CO., SAMUEL,   Worcester, MA

Flagg is believed to have been the first machine tool maker in Worcester, MA. He began operation in 1839 and, in 1847, formed SAMUEL FLAGG & CO. as a partnership with Lucius W. Pond, Ephrain H. Bellows, and Henry Holland. Flagg sold out to Pond after the shop burned in 1854. Pond continued business under the Flagg name until he reorganized as L.W. POND in 1856. Flagg, with others, formed the WORCESTER MACHINIST TOOL CO. in 1856. The firm made a variety of machine tools, including lathes such as that shown below.

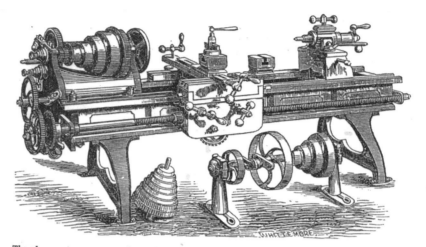

The above cut represents a Screw Cutting Engine Lathe, of 24 in. Swing, 12 ft. bed, with an improved Gib or Lock Rest so annexed that the Tool can be raised or altered when in operation, with the same ease and convenience as with the Weighted Rest; the lower part or half of the Rest is so constructed that the upper part can be easily removed, leaving the lower part well arranged for Boring purposes. The above cut represents the style of our Lathes under 40 in. Swing. We can furnish Weighted or Gibed Rests with Lathes under 36 in. Swing. Weighs 2700 lbs.

FLATHER & CO.,   Nashua, NH

A partnership of Edward W. Flather (1839-1902) and his brothers, William J. (1841-1912), Mark Jr. (1851-1926) and Joseph (1837-1907). formed in 1867 to make engine lathes, hand lathes, foot lathes and tapping machines. Planers and shapers were introduced later. The firm was incorporated in 1900 with Joseph Flather as president, and it operated into the mid-1920s. Mark Flather had left in 1884 to found the MARK FLATHER PLANER CO.; William J. Flather left in 1900 and joined the E.J. FLATHER MFG. CO., which was operated by his son.

Products offered in 1884 included 15" (Fig.1), 18" and 20" (Fig.2) engine lathes, and 15" lathes with an optional turret head in place of the tailstock (Fig.3).

The *NEW PATTERN* engine lathe was introduced in 1890 and offered in 14"-15" (Fig.4), 16", 20" (Fig.5), and 24"-28" swings. A cabinet style (Fig.6) with 22" swing was introduced in 1891. Taper attachments (Fig.7), turret attachments (Fig.8), 14" hand lathes with optional slide rests (Fig.9), 16" screw machines (Fig.10), and 26" turret head chucking lathes (Fig.11) were offered in 1893.

1903 production included NEW MODEL engine lathes from 14" (Fig.12) to 30" (Fig.13) sizes. A quick change feed gear engine lathe (Fig.14), was introduced in 1905. *(continued on next two pages)*

Fig.1
15 inch Swing, with 1¼ inch hole through Head Spindle.

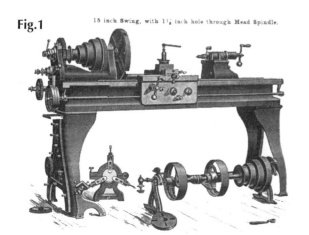

Fig.2
20 and 18 inch Swing, with 1½ inch hole through Head Spindle.

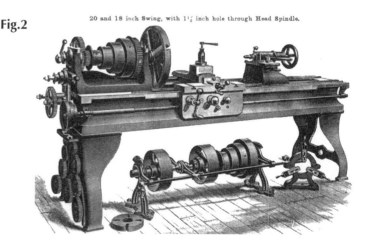

Fig.3

15 INCH LATHE WITH TURRET HEAD IN PLACE OF TAIL STOCK.

Fig.4

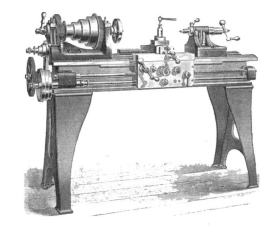

Fig.5

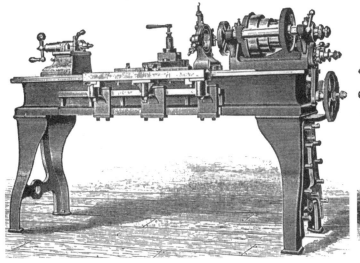

Fig.6

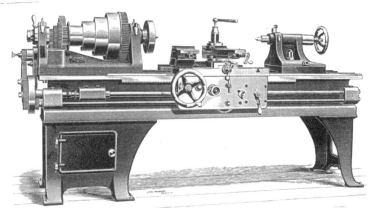

Flather Lathe, with Taper Attachment. **Fig.7**

Flather Lathe, with Turret Attachment. **Fig.8**

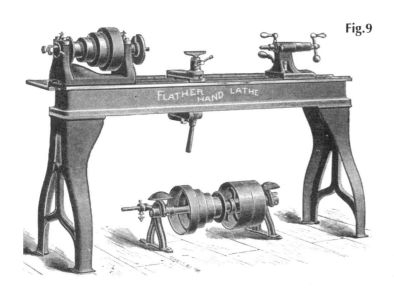

Fig.9

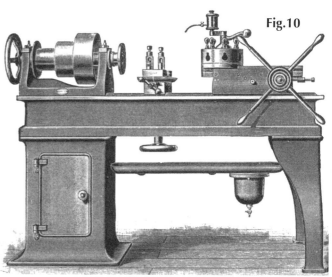

Fig.10

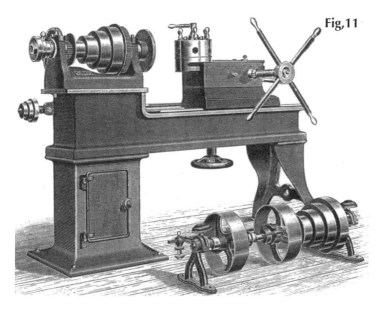

Fig,11

New Model

Fig.12

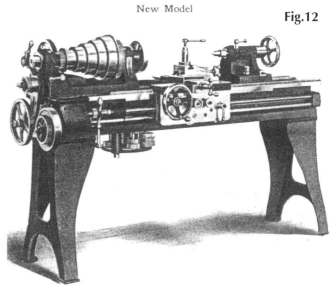

Fig.13

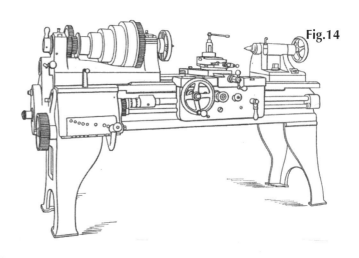

Fig.14

FLORENCE MACHINE CO., Florence, MA

Maker of 12" engine lathes (Fig.1) introduced in 1897 "to meet the needs of bicycle manufacturers." It was offered in 4', 5' and 6' bed lengths and with a turret head which could be mounted in place of the tail stock.

In 1898, the firm introduced a special tap threading lathe (Fig.2) which was equipped with a rotary magazine containing eight 14" lead screws, and eight half-nuts. This allowed cutting of very accurate pitches without complicated set-ups.

Fig.1

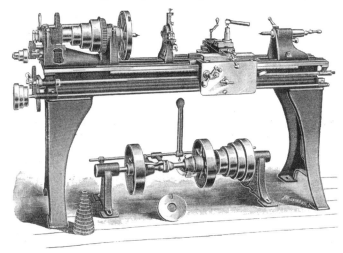

THE FLORENCE 12-INCH LATHE

Fig.2

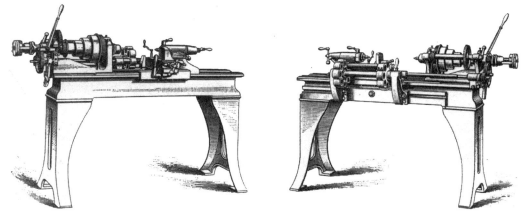

Front View   *Rear View.*

FOSDICK MACHINE TOOL CO., Cincinnati, OH

Formed by Phillip C. Fosdick (1858-1917) in 1902 as a reorganization of Fosdick & Holloway. Fosdick left when the firm was incorporated in 1905 but remained the largest single stockholder until he sold his interest to Arthur T. Leatherby in 1908.

The company specialized in drilling machines, especially large radial drills. In 1905, however, a 16" engine lathe *(below)* equipped with the Emmes patent quick change feed gear box was introduced. This appears to have been the only lathe built by Fosdick.

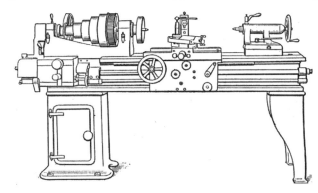

FOSTER-KIMBALL MACHINE CO., Chicago, IL, later
FOSTER MACHINE CO., Elkhart, IN

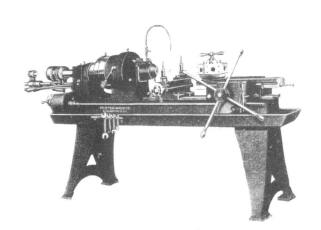

Formed in 1902 by William H. Foster (1871-1944) and Dean G. Kimball (1867-1933). Both had been employed by PEARSON MACHINE CO., a maker of small screw machines. The firm moved to Elkhart, IN, in 1906. Kimball sold out to Foster in 1907 and the firm was reorganized as the FOSTER MACHINE CO. in 1909.

Products included small screw machines, similar to those made by Pearson, and a line of turret lathes such as shown at right. The company was taken over by the International Machine Tool Corp. in 1940.

FOX & CO., GEO. H., Boston, MA

Operated by George H. Fox from 1845 to 1864 when it was reorganized as the AMERICAN TOOL & MACHINE CO. Maker of the FOX brassworker's lathe patented January 3, 1854. The FOX name for a lathe was one of very few to become a generic term.

FRECH, WILLIAM, Chicago, IL

Maker, beginning about 1884, of combination monitor and hand lathes, offered in two sizes. The No.1 bench lathe (Fig.) with 10" swing and the No.2 free-standing lathe (Fig.) with 12" swing. Note the removable tail stock, mounted turret offered as an option with both machines.

Fig.1

Fig.2

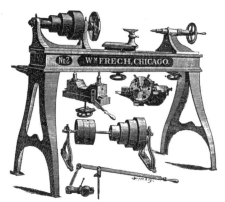

FREELAND TOOL WORKS, New York, NY

Founded about 1845 by Aaron M. Freeland (?-1871), the firm is believed to be the first machine tool builder in New York City, and made a variety of machine tools, including planers and engine lathes.

Freeland was reported to have copied his designs from English machine tools. A 20" engine lathe, made in 1853 and illustrated below, shows the English influence by its use of flat bed ways. Nearly all American lathes of the time were made with inverted Vee ways.

In 1871, Freeland's widow advertised the business, patterns, drawings, and stock for sale.

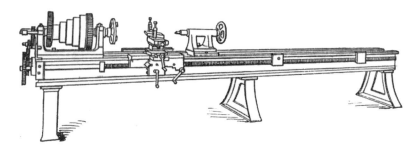

FULLER & WILSON, Worcester, MA, later
FULLER & CO., J.A., Worcester, MA

A partnership of James A. Fuller (1824-1912) and James E. Wilson, formed in 1881 to make 18" engine lathes and planers. In 1882 the firm reorganized as J.A. FULLER & CO., which operated until about 1899.

GAGE, JOHN H., Nashua, NH, later
GAGE, WARNER & WHITNEY, Nashua, NH

Founded by John H. Gage (1815-1862) who began making lathes and other machine tools under his own name in 1837. In 1851 Gage formed a partnership, GAGE, WARNER & WHITNEY, with David A.G. Warner and George Whitney. The firm, which is believed to be the first American firm devoted exclusively to the manufacture of machine tools, reorganized as WARNER, WHITNEY & CO. when Gage died in 1872.

GAGE MACHINE WORKS, Waterford, NY

Founded in 1835 by George Gage (1804-1892) to make a variety of machinery, the firm was advertising swivel head engine lathes as early as 1871 (Fig.1). For a time around 1850 Gage operated as GAGE & CAMPBELL, but was again sole owner of the GAGE MACHINE WORKS by 1871. In 1888, he turned the business over to his son, John E. Gage, who operated it until he sold out in 1896. The new owners, SNYDER & METCALF, used the GAGE name until at least 1905. 1880s production included 15" and 18" swivel-head lathes in both engine (Fig.2) and turret (Fig.3) style, and 15" *FOX* turret lathes (Fig.4).

Fig.1

Fig.2

Fig.3

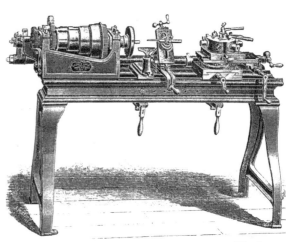

Fox Turret Lathe.

Fig.4

GARVIN & CO., E.E., New York, NY, later
GARVIN MACHINE CO., New York, NY

A partnership of Eugene E. Garvin (1858-1916) and his brother George K. Garvin (1859-1919), formed in 1879 as a reorganization of SMITH & GARVIN. In 1889, the firm became a stock company, the GARVIN MACHINE CO., with George K. Garvin as president and Eugene E. Garvin as vice president. Capital was increased from $100,000 to $500,000 in 1899. The company failed in 1925.

The firms specialized in milling machines, but a number of screw machines and lathes were also offered. These included 10" hand lathes offered in 1880 (Fig.1) and an improved version (Fig.2) introduced in 1882. The No.1 screw machine/monitor lathe (Fig.3) with

5/8" capacity was offered in 1889. The No.3 screw machine, with 2 1/8" capacity, was introduced in 1893 in power turret feed (Fig.4), wire feed, and chucking bar feed (Fig.5) models.

The 1900 catalog offered No.00 (Fig.6), No.1 (Fig.7), No.2 (Fig.8), No.13 (Fig.9), and No.14 screw machines (Fig.10); 2" x 12" universal screw machines (Fig.11); and No.21 (Fig.12) and No.22 (Fig.13) monitor lathes. 12" engine lathes (Fig.14) were introduced in 1903.

New products offered in the 1906 catalog included No.2 and 2½ double turret screw machines (Fig.15), No.2 and 2½ chasing bar screw machines, No.2½ and 12½ screw machines (Fig.16), and improved No.3 screw machines (Fig.17). Hand lathes were available in 10", 12" (Fig.18), and 15" swings and with optional slide rests (Fig.19). Attachments available in 1906 included elliptic chucks (Fig.20) for lathes 16" or larger. *(continued on the next three pages)*

Fig.1
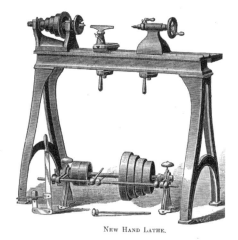
NEW HAND LATHE.

Fig.2

IMPROVED 10-INCH HAND LATHE.

Fig.3
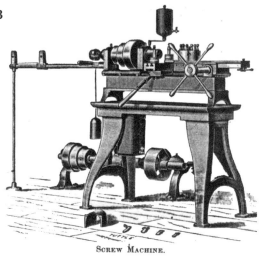
SCREW MACHINE.

Fig.4

Fig.5
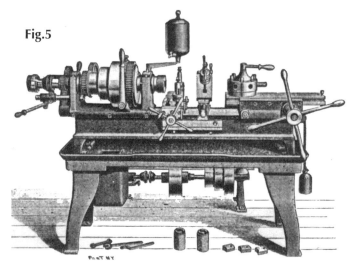

Fig.6
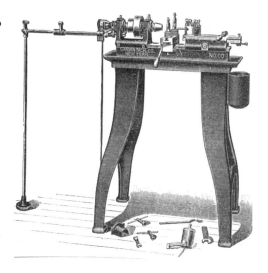

Fig.7

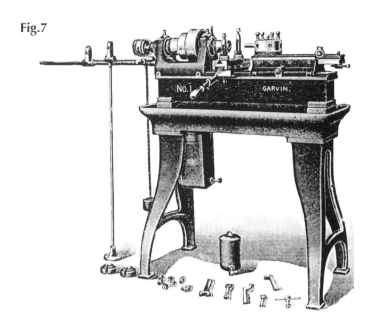

Fig.8

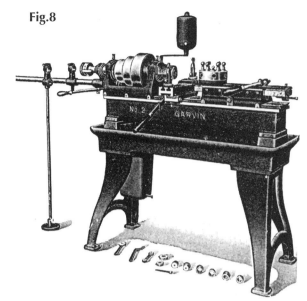

Fig.9

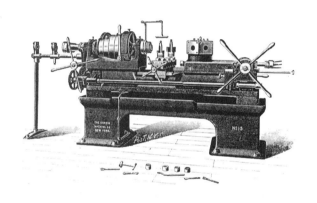

Fig.10

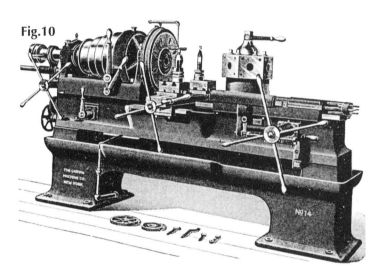

Fig.11

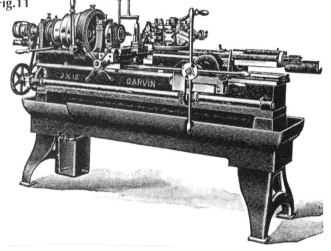

Fig.12

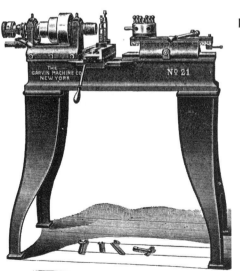

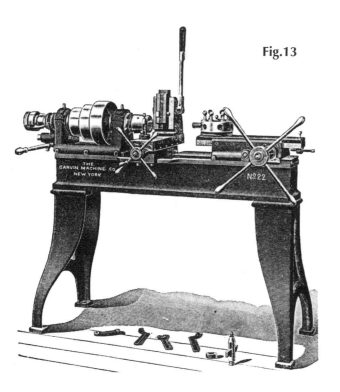

Fig.13

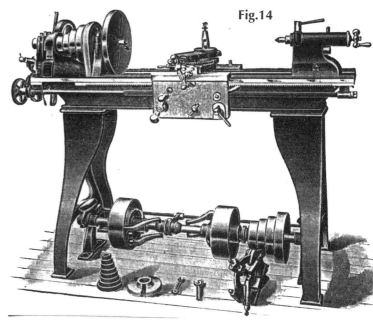

Fig.14

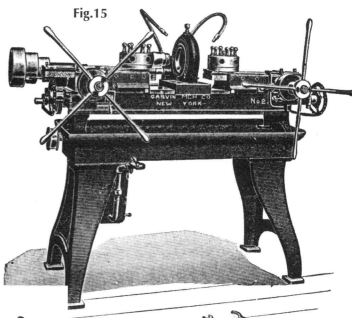

Fig.15

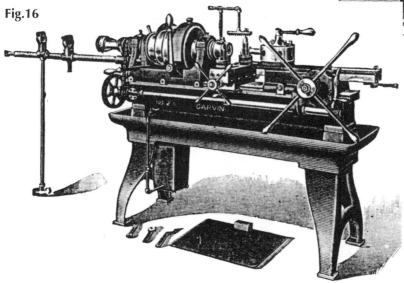

Fig.16

Fig.17

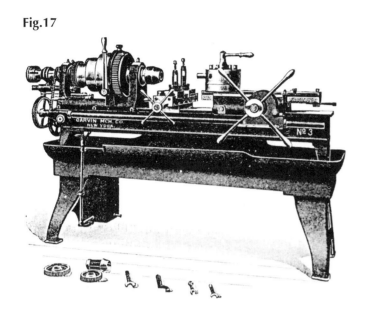

Fig.18

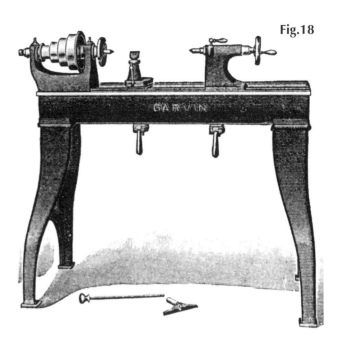

Fig.19

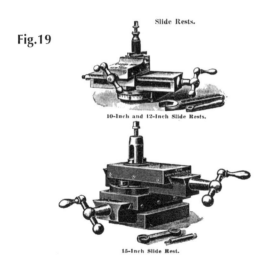

Slide Rests.

10-Inch and 12-Inch Slide Rests.

15-Inch Slide Rest.

Oval or Elliptic Chuck.

Fig.20

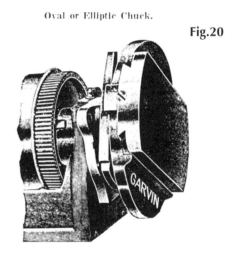

GAY, IRA & ZIBA, North Chelmsford, MA, later
GAY, SILVER & CO., North Chelmsford, MA

A partnership of brothers Ira Gay (?-1835) and Ziba Gay (?-1857), formed in 1830 to make textile machinery, lathes and other machine tools.

The firm reorganized as GAY, SILVER & CO. when Ira Gay died in 1835 and was replaced by Harvey Silver. Frederick W. Howe learned the machinist trade here before joining ROBBINS & LAWRENCE about 1853. The firm was again reorganized, as SILVER, GAY & CO., in 1857 when Ziba Gay died and was replaced by his son Ziba, Jr. (1823-1902).

Products included chain-driven engine lathes, including a 48" swing with granite bed, made about 1834 and still in use in 1896.

GAYLORD, CROSS & SPIERS, Waterbury, CT

Formed in 1882 by the merger of the Gaylord Foundry and the Cross & Spiers Machine Works. Products included small lathes and small drilling machines.

GERRY & SON, GEORGE, Athol Depot, MA

Maker, in 1876, of small, foot-power, drilling lathes and engine lathes.

GISHOLT MACHINE CO., Madison, WI

Founded in 1889 by John A. Johnson (1832-1901) to make heavy duty turret lathes. Johnson, who named the company after his hometown in Norway, was also co-owner of Fuller & Johnson, a large farm machinery maker.

Early turret lathes were designed by Conrad M. Conradson (1861-1940) who was superintendent from 1889 until he left in 1895. Conradson later organized the AMERICAN TURRET LATHE MFG. CO. The next generation machines were designed by Charles L. Libbey who left in 1906 to be one of the founders of the INTERNATIONAL MACHINE TOOL CO.

Johnson's sons Carl A. (1870-1931), Maurice I. (1877-1935), Frederick A. (1862-1908), and Hobart S. (1873-1942) served in various executive positions in the company. A third generation was active when the firm closed about 1970.

Introduced in 1891, the Conradson turret lathe was offered in a gap model (Fig.1) with swings from 20" to 50", a short bed 20" swing model (Fig.2), a combination model (Fig.3) with five swings from 12" to 30" and a turret-only model (Fig.4) with five swings from 12" to 30". An improved model (Fig.5), with five swings from 13" to 34", was offered in 1896, and an electric motor driven model (Fig.6) was introduced in 1901. *(Illustrations continued on next page)*

THE CONRADSON LATHE.

Fig.1

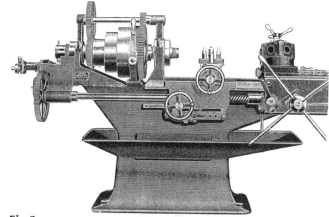

Fig.2

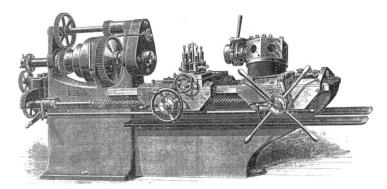

Fig.3

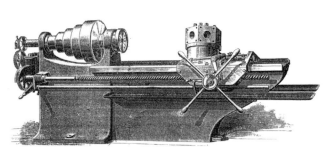

Fig.4

Fig.5

Fig.6

GLEASON, WILLIAM,   Rochester, NY, later
GLEASON TOOL CO.,   Rochester, NY

Formed in 1875 by William Gleason (1836-1922) when he took over the Kidd Iron Works. Gleason's primary products were gear cutting machines, but for a time he also offered engine lathes, planers and drilling machines.

A line of large engine lathes was introduced in 1887; included were 26" swing (Fig.1), 32"-38" swing (Fig.2) with double back gears, and 42"-48"-52"-60"-72" swings (Fig.3) with triple gearing. 32" x 8' shafting lathes (Fig.4) were offered in 1893.

The firm was reorganized as the GLEASON TOOL CO. in 1890 and incorporated as the GLEASON WORKS in 1903. In 1900, Gleason sold his lathe and planer lines to the PITTSBURG MACHINE TOOL CO.

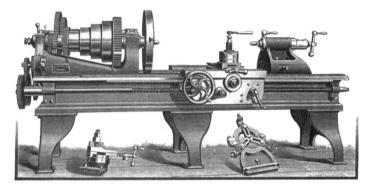

Gleason Screw Cutting Engine Lathe, 26 Inch Swing, 12 Foot Bed.

Fig.1

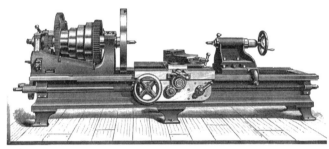

Gleason Screw Cutting Engine Lathe, 38 Inch Swing, 14 Foot Bed.
WITH DOUBLE BACK GEARS, COMPOUND REST, AND POWER CROSS FEED.

Fig.2

Gleason Triple Geared Engine Lathe, 60 Inch Swing, 16 Foot Bed, Cone on Side Spindle.
THIS LATHE HAS COMPOUND TOOL BLOCK, WITH POWER CROSS AND ANGULAR FEEDS.

Fig.3

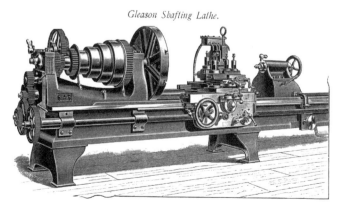

Gleason Shafting Lathe.

Fig.4

GODDARD MACHINE CO.,   Holyoke, MA

Formed in 1889 by Joel S. Webber to make a line of engine lathes such as the 15" swing model shown below. The company failed in 1906.

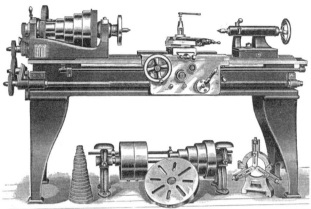

GODDARD, SHAW & CO.,   Brockton, MA

A partnership of George O. Goddard and Kenelm W. Shaw formed about 1875. Maker of 17" swing engine lathes with the lead screw centered between the ways. The firm dissolved in 1882 and Shaw continued the business as SHAW & LAMBERT.

GOMERSALL, A.,   Germantown, PA

Lathe builder operating in 1882.

GOULD & EBERHARDT, E.,   Newark, NJ, later
GOULD & EBERHARDT,   Newark, NJ

A partnership of Ezra Gould (1808-1901), Ulrich Eberhardt (1841-1901), and Henry E. Eberhardt (1851-1934), formed when Gould took the Eberhardts as partners in 1877. The firm reorganized as GOULD & EBERHARDT when Gould retired in 1890. Production centered around a line of shapers, but hand lathes, shown below, were also offered.

SIXTEEN-INCH QUICK-STOPPING HAND LATHE.

GRANT & BOGERT,   Flushing, L.I., NY

A partnership of John J. Grant (1844-1934) and John L. Bogert, formed in 1881 to make engine lathes. Products included 14", weighted carriage engine lathes (Fig.) introduced in 1882 and long bed, 26" engine lathes (Fig.) introduced in 1883. Grant left the firm in 1884. Bogert continued operation under his own name. *(Illustrations on next page)*

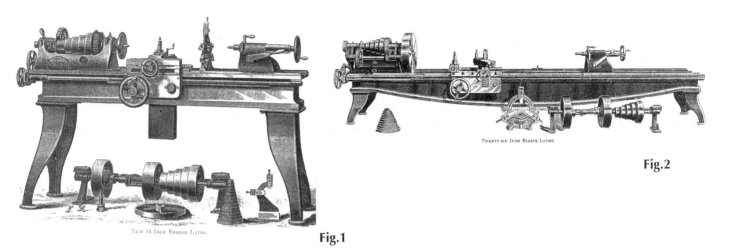

Fig.1

Fig.2

GRANT MACHINE TOOL WORKS, Cleveland, OH, later
GRANT TOOL CO., Franklin, PA

Founded July 30, 1898, by John J. Grant (1844-1934) after he had founded, or worked for, a number of companies since leaving GRANT & BOGERT. Products included 44" turret chucking lathes (Fig.1).

The company reorganized as the GRANT TOOL CO. in 1900 and moved to Franklin, PA, where it failed in 1903. Products included 16" taper turning lathes (Fig.2).

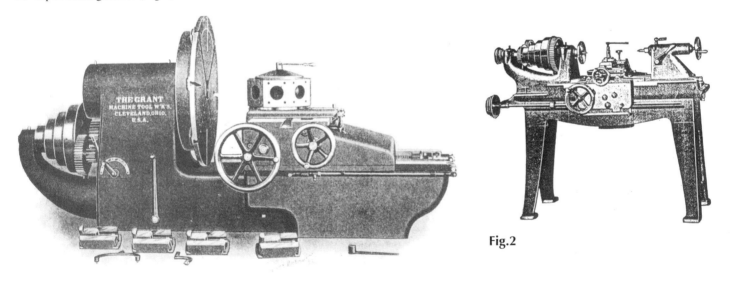

Fig.2

Fig.1

GRAY, Jr. & CO., G.A., Cincinnati, OH, later
GRAY CO., G.A., Cincinnati, OH

Founded in 1881 by George A. Gray Jr. (1839-1905) who had previously been associated with the NILES TOOL WORKS and the UNIVERSAL RADIAL DRILL CO. His first product was a 17" engine lathe offered in 1881 (Fig.1). An improved model was offered by 1884 (Fig.2). Other products included boring and turning lathes (Fig.3) offered in 1887. Gray reorganized as the G.A. GRAY CO. in 1886 and soon began to specialize in planers. *(Illustrations continued on next page)*

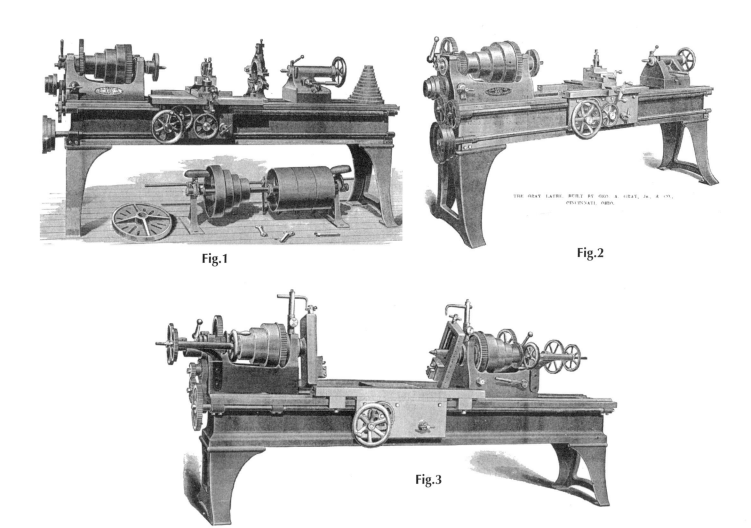

Fig.1

Fig.2

THE GRAY LATHE, BUILT BY GEO. A. GRAY, Jr., & CO.,
CINCINNATI, OHIO.

Fig.3

GREAVES, KLUSMAN & CO., Cincinnati, OH

A partnership of William A. Greaves (1862-1922) and Herman H. Klusman (1864-1918), formed in 1889 to make woodworking machinery and, later, engine lathes. In 1914, the firm incorporated as the GREAVES-KLUSMAN TOOL CO. Products included 17" engine lathes with a patent feeding and screw cutting device, offered in 1900 (Fig.1) and standard engine lathes from 16" to 24" swing (Fig.2) offered in 1908. A 14" model was added in 1910.

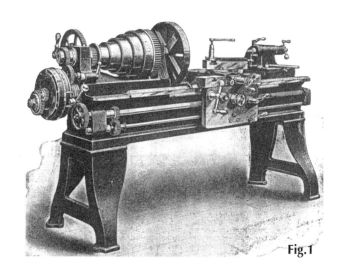

Fig.1

Standard Engine Lathes
16 to 24 inch Swing

Built by

Greaves, Klusman & Co.

S. E. Cor. Cook & Alfred Sts.
CINCINNATI, OHIO, U. S. A.

Also Builders of Pattern Makers' Lathes and
Machinery and Metal Spinners' Lathes

Fig.2

HADLEY FALLS MACHINE CO., Holyoke, MA

A large machine shop built in 1850 as the textile machinery-making arm of the Hadley Falls Co. Some machine tools, including lathes, were made c1855. The parent company went bankrupt in 1857 leaving the machine shop idle until it was bought by P. Whitin & Sons in 1860.

HAMILTON MACHINE TOOL CO., Hamilton, OH

Formed about 1890 to make a line of upright drills. By 1898, the firm was also making lathes. The 1899 catalog offered engine lathes in 14" (Fig.1), 18" type A (Fig.2) and type B (Fig.3) styles, 26" type A and type B (Fig.4) styles, and a triple geared 32" (Fig.5) model.

The entire line was redesigned in 1903 to incorporate quick change feed gears and heavier construction for use with high speed steel cutting tools (Fig.6).

The firm incorporated in 1903 with capital of $300,000 and reorganized as the HAMILTON TOOL CO. in 1927. Charles F. Hilker was president from 1903 to about 1927. *(Illustrations continued on next page)*

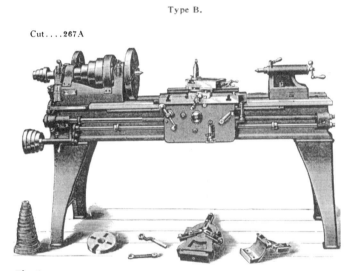

14-Inch x 6-Foot " Hamilton " Engine Lathe.

Type B.

Cut....267A

Fig.1

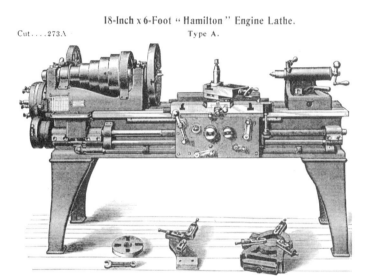

18-Inch x 6-Foot " Hamilton " Engine Lathe.

Type A.

Cut....273.A

Fig.2

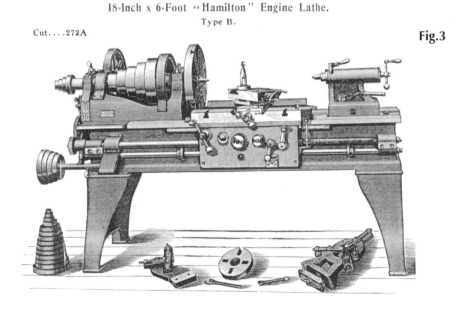

18-Inch x 6-Foot " Hamilton " Engine Lathe.

Type B.

Cut....272A

Fig.3

26-Inch x 10-Foot " Hamilton " Engine Lathe.

Type A.

Fig.4

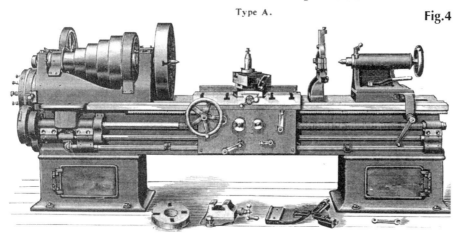

32-Inch x 12-Foot " Hamilton " Engine Lathe.

Triple Geared.

Fig.5

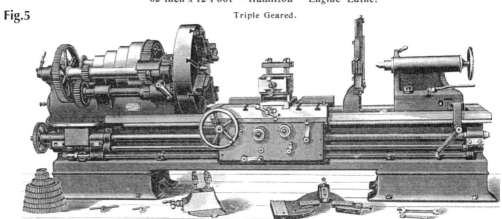

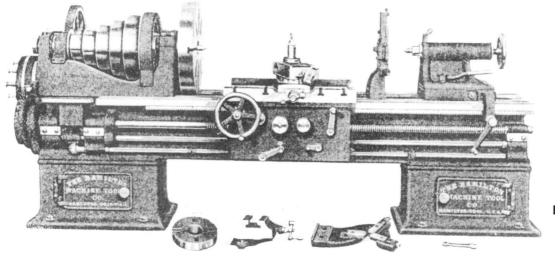

Fig.6

HAND MFG. CO., S. ASHTON,   Toughkenamon, PA

Formed about 1880 by S. Ashton Hand (1856-1940) to make engine lathes. Products included 14" lathes offered in 1881 (Fig.1), and improved 14" model introduced in 1882 (Fig.2), and a further improved model offered in 1886 (Fig.3).

The firm was closed by 1895 when Hand started a business specializing in photography of machinery. Hand later served as an associate editor of "American Machinist" magazine from 1918 until his death in 1940. *(Illustrations continued on next page)*

Screw Cutting Engine Lathe. **Fig.1**

Improved Engine Lathe **Fig.2**

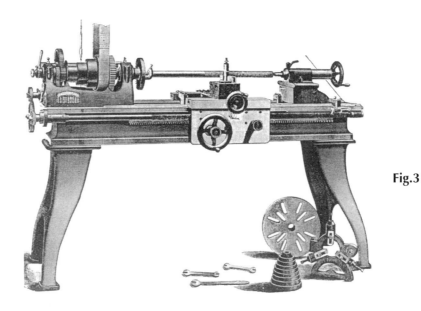

Fig.3

HARDIE, P., Albany, NY

Maker, in 1860, of "screw-cutting lathes, 6-feet long, 14" swing, with swing heads." Price was $150.

HARDINGE BROTHERS, Chicago, IL, later Elmira, NY

Formed in July, 1890, by Franklin Hardinge and his brother Henry H. Hardinge. Early products were watchmakers' tools and watchmakers' small foot lathes. In 1902, the brothers bought the *CATARACT* lathe line from the defunct CATARACT TOOL & OPTICAL CO. and began producing the No.3, 7" bench lathe (Fig.1). An improved No.4 version was offered by 1907 (Fig.2). Accessories for the bench lathes included screw slotting and milling devices (Fig.3), six inch turrets (Fig.4), double tool cross slides (Fig.5), and screw cutting attachments (Fig.6). Henry left the firm in 1895; Franklin was serving as chairman when the firm moved to Elmira, NY, in 1931. *(Illustrations continued on next page)*

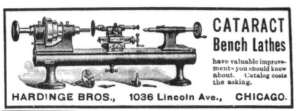

CATARACT Bench Lathes have valuable improvements you should know about. Catalog costs the asking.

HARDINGE BROS., 1036 Lincoln Ave., CHICAGO. **Fig.1**

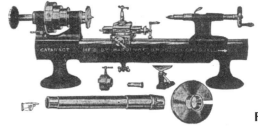

Fig.2

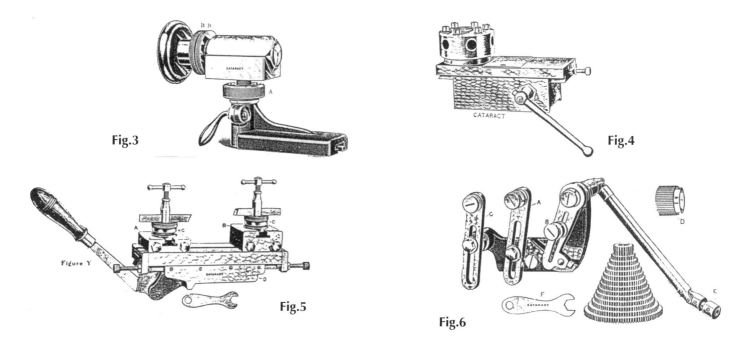

Fig.3

Fig.4

Figure Y

Fig.5

Fig.6

HARRINGTON & HASKINS, Philadelphia, PA

A partnership of Edward Harrington and Hugh S. Haskins formed in 1867 to make engine lathes. The firm reorganized as EDWARD HARRINGTON & SON about 1875.

HARRINGTON & SON, EDWARD, Philadelphia, PA, later
HARRINGTON, SON & CO., E., Philadelphia, PA, later
HARRINGTON, SON & CO., EDWIN., Philadelphia, PA

Formed about 1875 by Edward Harrington and his son Edwin Harrington (1854-1899). In 1882, the firm reorganized as E. HARRINGTON, SON & CO. and, about 1891, as EDWIN HARRINGTON, SON & CO., INC. that operated into the 1920s.

Early products included turret lathes with horizontal axis turrets (Fig.1) introduced about 1875, 28"/48" extension gap lathes with sliding beds (Fig.2) introduced about 1878, and 25" facing lathes (Fig.3) offered in 1884. By 1893, the extension gap lathe had been redesigned (Fig.4) and was offered in 22"/36", 28"/48", 36"/60" and 48"/72" sizes.

A line of heavy engine lathes was in production by 1894 and included 16" swing (Fig.5) with an optional taper attachment (Fig.6), 20" swing, 38" swing (Fig.7), and 48" swing (Fig.8). A 28" shafting lathe (Fig.9) with a gear driven spindle in the tailstock was offered in 1896. *(Illustrations continued on next two pages)*

Fig.1

Fig.2

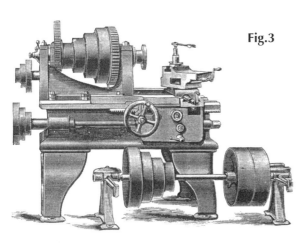

Fig.3

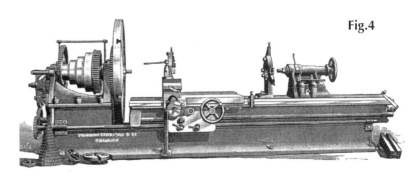

Fig.4

Fig.5

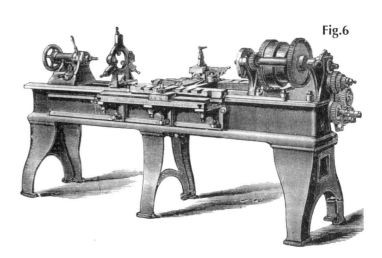

Fig.6

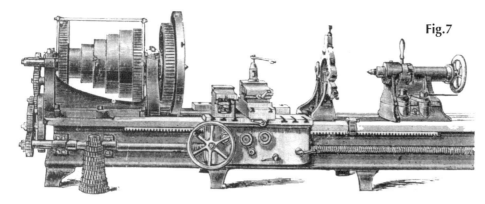

Fig.7

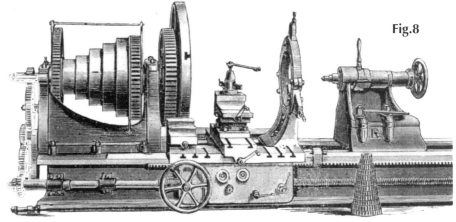

Fig.8

Fig.9

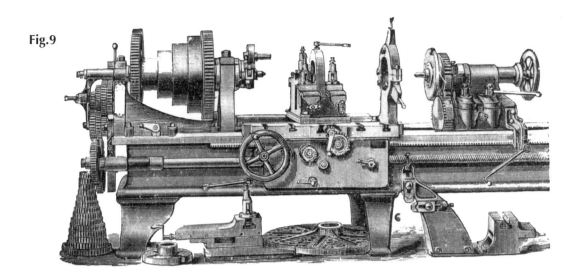

HARRIS & CO., D.L.,   Springfield, MA

A partnership comprising D.L. Harris, R.F. Hawkins, and W.H. Burrall. Maker, in 1865, of lathes, planers and a variety of other machinery.

HARRIS & CO., J.F.,   Binghampton, NY

Maker of 12" and 14" engine lathes in 1890. Its output was sold through the LODGE & DAVIS MACHINE TOOL CO. and may have been marked with that name.

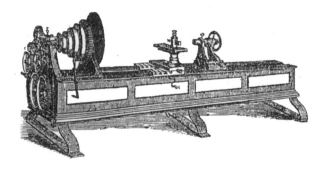

HARTSON-S PATENT LATHE.

HARTSON'S MACHINE SHOP,   New York, NY

Maker, in 1847, of Hartson's patent lathe, turning machines, and planing machines.

HASSELQUIST & CO., A.,   Elgin, IL

Founded in 1901 by Albert A Hasselquist (1863-1939) to make small lathes and other machinery for the Elgin, IL, watch industry. The firm reorganized as the ELGIN TOOL WORKS in 1904 and incorporated in 1906 with Hasselquist as president.

HAWES & CO., WM. M.,   Fall River, MA

Maker, beginning in 1865, of engine lathes, hand lathes, planers and other machine tools.

HECKENDORN & WILHELM,   Reading, PA

A partnership of Henry C. Heckendorn and William H. Wilhelm, formed about 1880 to make light duty engine lathes such as shown on next page. The partnership was dissolved in 1887.

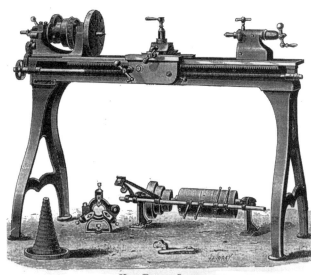

NEW ENGINE LATHE.

HENDEY MACHINE CO.,   Torrington, CT

Formed in 1870 as a partnership of Henry J. Hendey (1844-1906) and his brother Arthur Hendey (1846-1926). The firm was incorporated August 22, 1874. Arthur Hendey left in 1875. Henry J. Hendey continued to operate the firm and served as president until his death in 1906.

Shapers and planers were the primary products in the early years, but spinning lathes and hand lathes in 12" (Fig.1) and 15" swings were offered by 1880.

Wendell P. Norton ((1861-?) joined the firm in 1886. The first *NORTON* lathe, a semi-automatic design, was introduced in 1887 (Fig.2). A Norton-designed 15" turret lathe (Fig.3) was introduced in 1888. Norton left in 1889 to start his own firm, W.P. NORTON CO., but returned to Hendey in 1892 as superintendent. In 1892, Norton received a patent for a geared feed lathe with lever shifting, probably the first successful design. The *HENDEY-NORTON* lathe, as it came to be known, was introduced in 1893. Offered in 12" (Fig.4), 14" (Fig.5), 16", 18", 20", and 24", 32" (Fig.6) swings it became a Hendey staple for many years. In 1901, the first electric drive version (Fig.7) of the *HENDEY-NORTON* was offered.

In 1899, Hendey announced that it was sole owner of the Peter and William L. Shellenback engine lathe patents previously owned by the SHELLENBACK MACHINE TOOL CO.

Other lathes included 14" engine lathes (Fig.8), 16" and 21" cabinet (Fig.9) lathes, and 20"/36" turret chucking lathes (Fig.10) offered in 1892. An all-geared head, electrically driven model (Fig.11), offered in 12", 14", 16", 18" and 20" swings, was introduced in 1907.
(Illustrations continued on next two pages)

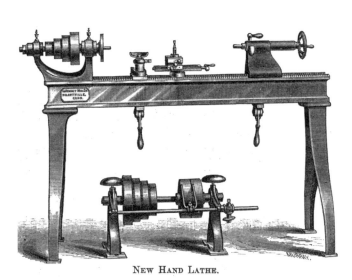

NEW HAND LATHE.

Fig.1

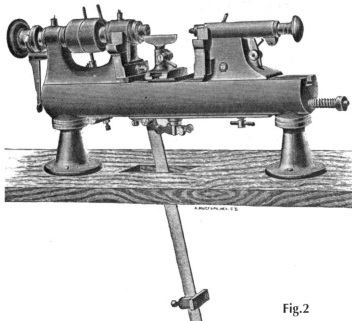

Fig.2

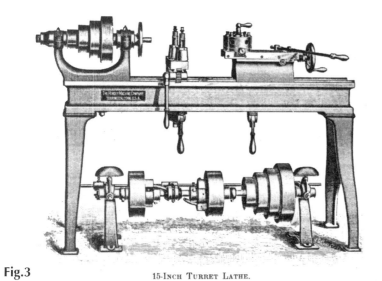

Fig.3

15-INCH TURRET LATHE.

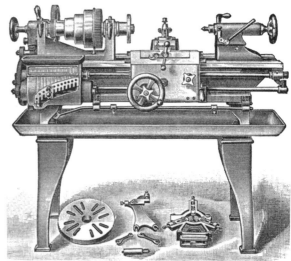

Fig.4

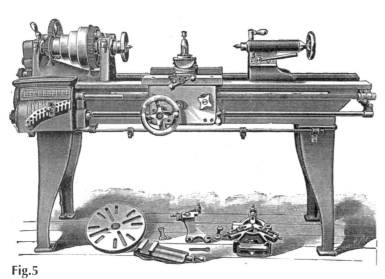

Fig.5

Fig.6

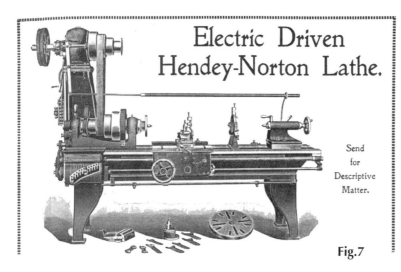

Electric Driven
Hendey-Norton Lathe.

Send
for
Descriptive
Matter.

Fig.7

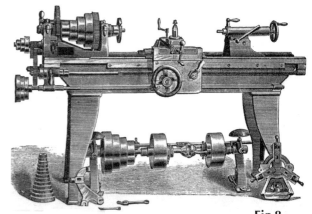

Fig.8

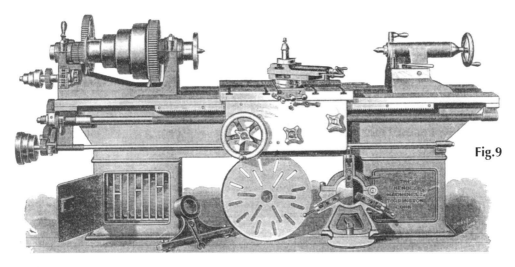

Fig.9

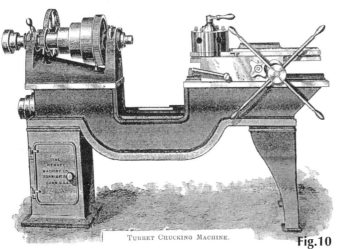

Turret Chucking Machine.

Fig.10

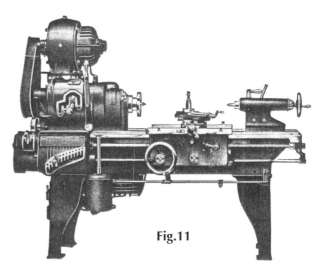

Fig.11

HENLEY MACHINE TOOL WORKS,   Richmond, IN

Formed in 1890 by Micajah C. Henley (1857-1927) to take over the pulley lathe business of the RICHMOND CITY MILL WORKS. The *SHELLENBACK* pulley lathes were made under patents issued June 14, 1887, to Peter Shellenback and February 17, 1891, jointly to Shellenback and Henly. In 1895, Henley announced that he had stopped making lathes in order to concentrate on the manufacture of bicycles.

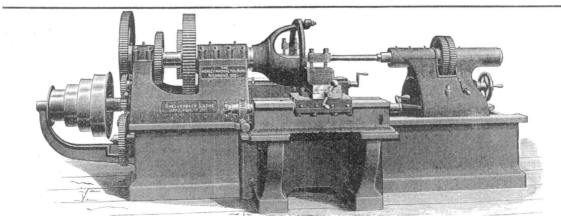

30 INCH, 42 INCH and 60 INCH PULLEY LATHES
For Simultaneously Boring and Turning Pulleys, both straight and crowning face, Cone Pulleys, Gear Blanks, and a variety of other work.
Manufactured by The HENLEY MACHINE TOOL WORKS, Richmond, Ind.

HEPWORTH & CO., S.S., Yonkers, NY

Formed in New York City in 1875, the firm moved to Yonkers, NY, in 1883. It failed in July, 1890, and all assets were sold at auction. Sugar mill machinery was the main product, but the firm also made extra heavy engine lathes (Fig.1) and large lathes for facing flanges (Fig.2) beginning about 1885.

Fig.1

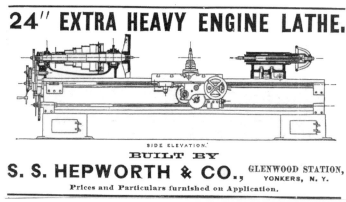

Fig.2

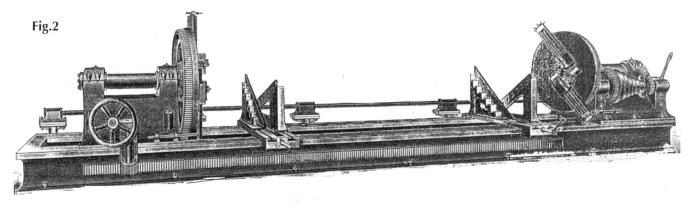

LATHE FOR FACING FLANGES.

HOFFMAN & BILLINGS MFG. CO., Milwaukee, WI

Operated by John C. Hoffman, president, the firm was primarily a steam engine builder. The firm entered the lathe business in 1891 when it introduced a large pit lathe with a 10' face plate and seven step cone pulley. With the pit, the machine could turn workpieces up to 26' in diameter.

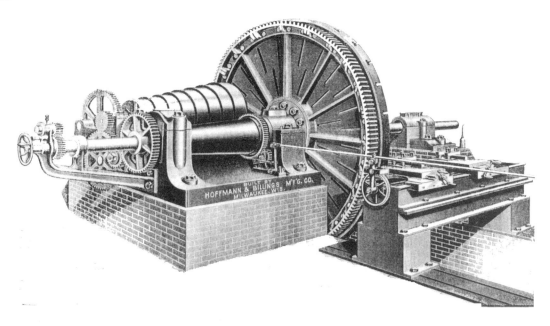

HOLMES TURRET TOOL POST CO.,   Chicago, IL

Maker, in 1895, of a turret tool holder attachment for lathes. Specifications are shown in the ad at right.

HOWARD, GEORGE C.,   Philadelphia, PA

Maker of lathes, planers, and drilling machines c1881-1883.

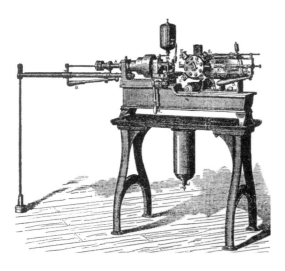

HUBBEL SCREW CO.,   New York, NY

Formed by N.C. Hubbel to make small screws. In 1874, Hubbel purchased a screw machine from PRATT & WHITNEY and modified it by moving the slide to a vertical position and adding provision for slotting the screws. He then began making the machine for sale. By 1876, the firm was advertising screw machines with a claimed capacity of 75 gross screws per day. *(see left)*

INTERNATIONAL MACHINE TOOL CO.,   Indianapolis, IN

Founded in October, 1906, by Orlando B. Iles (1869-1941), Charles L. Libbey, and William K. Millholland (1856-1916). Iles, an Indianapolis businessman served as general manager and later president; Libbey, who had been chief engineer at the GISHOLT MACHINE CO. was superintendent; Millholland sold out in 1909 and formed the W.K. Millholland Machine Co.

The company's first product, shown below, was the *LIBBEY* full swing, side carriage, turret lathe. [See STEINLE TURRET MACHINE CO. for a very similar turret lathe introduced by another ex-Gisholt employee at about the same time.]

The firm continued to produce heavy turret lathes until 1941, when it merged with the FOSTER MACHINE CO. and was reorganized as the International Machine Tool Corp.

JOHNSON & CO., A.J.,   Cleveland, OH
Maker, in 1897, of a portable, horizontal axis, turret attachment for engine lathes. The turret was manually fed towards the spindle and rotated automatically when it was retracted.

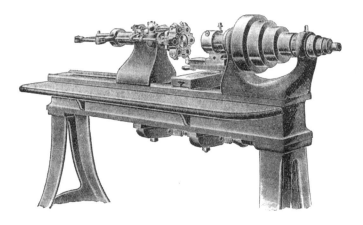

THE JOHNSON AUTOMATIC TURRET HEAD.

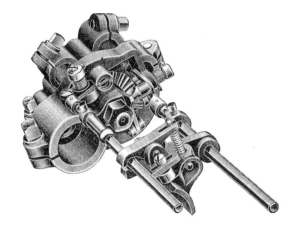

Rear View of Turret Head.

JOHNSON, E.E.,   Putnam, CT
Maker, in 1904, of the 10" foot power lathe shown at right.

10=Inch Screw Cutting Lathe

For light manufacturing. A splendid tool and a big value for the money. Send for circular and discounts.

E. E. JOHNSON, PUTNAM, CONN.

JOHNSON, JR. & CO., ISRAEL H.,   Philadelphia, PA, later
JOHNSON, JR. CO., ISRAEL H.,   Philadelphia, PA
Formed in 1878 by Israel H. Johnson, Jr. to make heavy machine tools for the Philadelphia ordnance and railroad industries. The firm incorporated as the ISRAEL H. JOHNSON, JR. CO. about 1910 and went out of business in 1926.

Five 50" swing, 22' bed, boring and turning lathes for 6-inch naval guns (Fig.1) were built in 1889. Johnson was paid $23,298 for the five machines. Products offered in 1890 included 17" bolt lathes designed to turn tapered bolts for locomotive construction (Fig.2) and

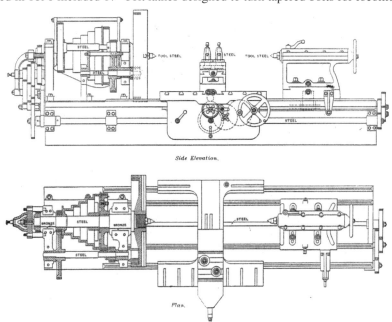

Side Elevation.

Plan.

Fig.1

TURNING AND BORING LATHE FOR 6-INCH BREECH-LOADING RIFLE HOOPS. BUILT BY ISRAEL H. JOHNSON, JR. & CO., PHILADELPHIA, PA.

16" single axle lathes with two carriages (Fig.3). Heavy duty 43" engine lathes (Fig.4) were introduced in 1892. By 1903 the engine lathe line was improved and had expanded to include 30", 33", 36", 48", 54" and 60" sizes.

In 1903 the firm offered an electrically driven lathe (Fig.5) with a constant speed motor and a quite complex five speed gear box which, with the back gears, gave ten operating speeds.

Fig.2

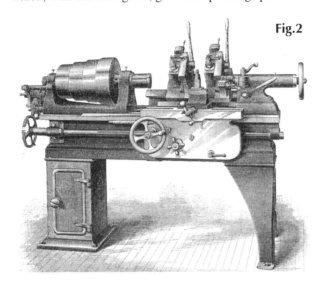

Fig.3

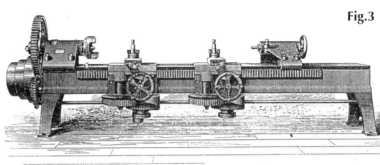

SINGLE AXLE LATHE WITH TWO CARRIAGES.

Fig.4

THE JOHNSON ENGINE LATHE.

Fig.5

JONES, LAMSON & CO., Windsor, VT, later
JONES & LAMSON MACHINE CO., Windsor, later Springfield, VT

A partnership of Ebenezer G. Lamson (1814-1892) and Russell L. Jones, formed in 1869 as a reorganization of the WINDSOR MFG. CO. The firm was a successor to ROBBINS & LAWRENCE CO., whose plant and equipment had been bought by Ebenezer G. Lamson in 1859. Henry D. Stone (1815-1899) continued as superintendent.

Early products included engine lathes, hand lathes, and chucking lathes based on Frederick W. Howe (1822-1891) designs done for Robbins & Lawrence and small turret lathes with self-revolving turrets based on Howe's 1855 design done for Robbins & Lawrence. The firm also made a variety of other machinery, most for quarrying.

Its 1875 catalog included engine lathes (Fig.1) in 14", 15", 17" and 20" swings and a new line of turret lathes/screw machines with power feed, patented October 20, 1874, by Henry D. Stone. The turret lathes were made in No.1 size with back gears and power feed (Fig.2), No.2 size with power feed (Fig.3) and without power feed (Fig.4), and No.5 size with power feed and an adjustable chuck patented January 30, 1872 (Fig.5).

In 1876, the machine tool portion of the company was split off and incorporated as the JONES & LAMSON MACHINE CO. Ralph H. Lamson, nephew of Ebenezer G. Lamson, was elected president. On November 18, 1887, Adna Brown (1828-1901) and Amasa Woolson (1811-1891) bought control from Ebenezer G. Lamson. They moved the company to Springfield, VT, in 1888 and increased the capital stock from $50,000 to $60,000. Woolson served as president until his death in 1891.

Production in 1884 included improved engine lathes (Fig.6) in 14", 15", 18", 20" and 24" swings, and turret lathes/screw machines in No.1 size with back gears and power feed (Fig.7), No.2 size with power feed (Fig.8), and No.4 and No.5 sizes with adjustable chucks (Fig.9). New, larger turret lathes in No.8 and No.9 sizes (Fig.10) and No.10 and No.11 sizes (Fig.11) were introduced in 1885 and a still larger 24" swing with 3¼" spindle hole model (Fig.12) in 1888.

James Hartness (1861-1934) joined the company in 1889 as superintendent. He was elected president in 1893, serving until his retirement in 1900. Under Hartness' leadership, a new line of turret lathes (Fig.13), designed for continuous bar feeding without stopping the machine, was introduced in 1889. In 1890 the new design was also available in large 24" turret lathes with 3¼" spindle hole (Fig.14), and turret screw machines (Fig.15) of the same size.

Improved, 20" turret screw machines, with 2¾" spindle hole (Fig.16), and 20" chucking lathes (Fig.17) were introduced in 1891. In 1891 the firm also introduced the now famous, Hartness designed, 2"x 24" "flat" turret lathe (Fig.18). This machine, in a variety of configurations, including a 3"x 36" size offered by 1907 (Fig.19), was a staple product for many years and the machine for which Jones & Lamson is best known. *(Illustrations continued on next three pages.)*

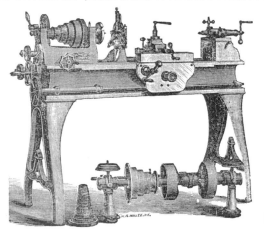

Fig.1

Fig.2

Fig.3

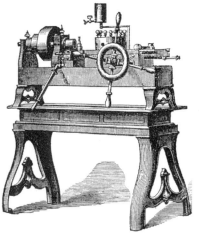

Fig.4

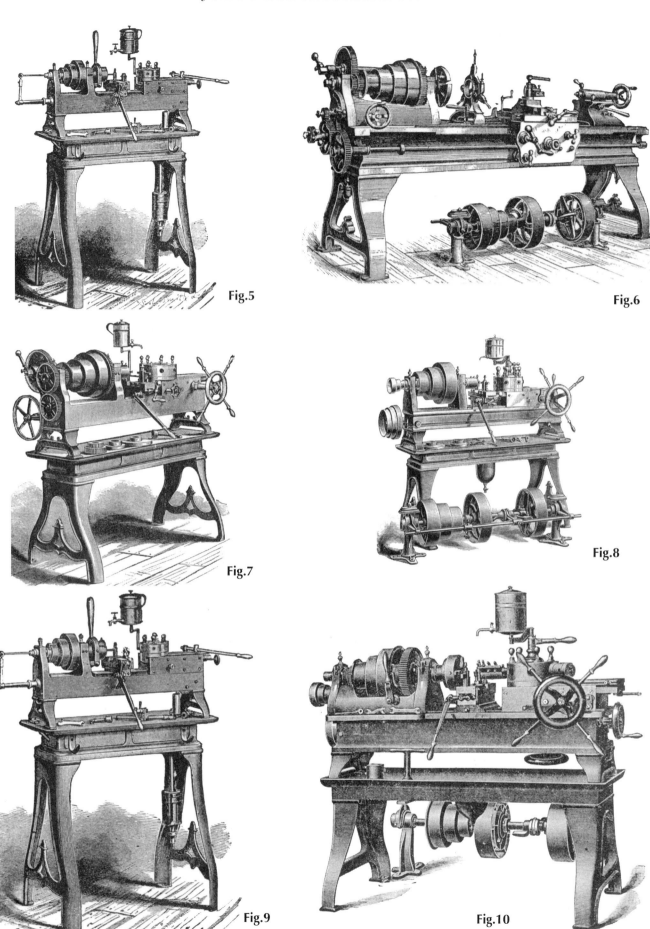

Fig.5

Fig.6

Fig.7

Fig.8

Fig.9

Fig.10

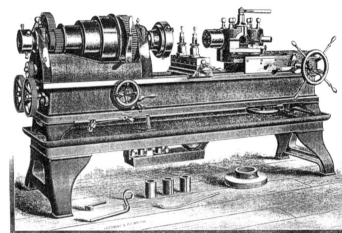

Fig.12

Fig.11

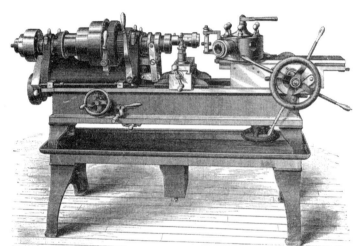

Fig.13

Fig.14

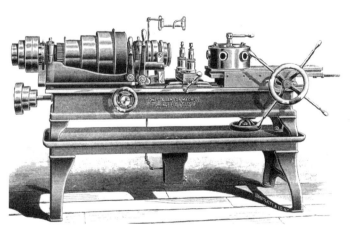

Fig.15

Fig.16

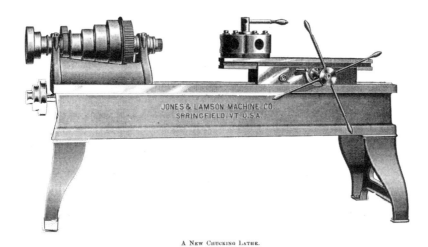

Fig.17

A New Chucking Lathe.

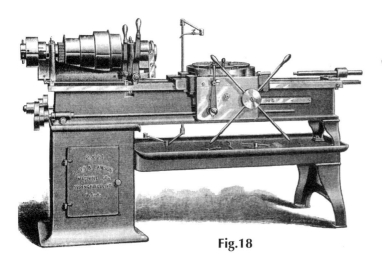

Fig.18

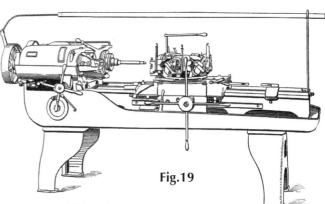

Fig.19

LAMSON, GOODNOW & YALE, Windsor, VT, later
LAMSON & CO., E.G., Windsor, VT

Formed in 1859 when Ebenezer G. Lamson (1814-1892), Abel F. Goodnow and B. Buchanan Yale bought the plant and equipment of the defunct ROBBINS & LAWRENCE CO. Henry D. Stone (1815-1899),who had worked at Robbins & Lawrence since 1847, was appointed superintendent, continuing through the later reorganizations. In 1862, the firm reported employment of "100 men making gun machinery." A variety of other machinery was also offered. Lamson bought out his partners and reorganized as E.G. LAMSON & CO. in 1864. In 1865 he again reorganized, this time as the WINDSOR MFG. CO.

All the firms made engine lathes and turret lathes, based on Frederick W. Howe and Henry D. Stone designs originally done for ROBBINS & LAWRENCE, including the Howe design turret lathe/screw machine shown at right.

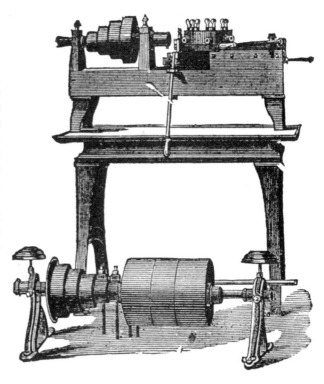

LATHE & MORSE, Worcester, MA, later
LATHE & MORSE TOOL CO., Worcester, MA

A partnership of Martin Lathe and Edwin Morse formed in 1864 as a successor to SHEPARD, LATHE & MORSE. In 1871, the firm reorganized as a stock company, the LATHE & MORSE TOOL CO. Employment in 1882 was 40 to 50 men. The company was defunct in March, 1891, when the assets were sold to William F. Draper, who then formed the DRAPER MACHINE TOOL CO.

Products included a variety of machine tools, primarily planers and lathes. Lathe production included 15" (Fig.1), 20" (Fig.2), and 24" (Fig.3) engine lathes offered in 1872. Production in 1890 included 15" (Fig.4) and 21" (Fig.5) engine lathes.

Fig.1

Fig.2

Fig.3

Fig.4

TWENTY-ONE INCH SWING SCREW-CUTTING ENGINE LATHE.—With Compound Power Cross Feed Rest.

Fig.5

LATTA, A.B. & E.,
(BUCKEYE WORKS) Cincinnati, OH

Operated by Alexander B. Latta (1821-1865). Maker of "all kinds of lathes and machinists' tools" c1845-1865. Production included a 90" locomotive driving wheel lathe made in 1848. Note the unusual form of headstock shown at right.

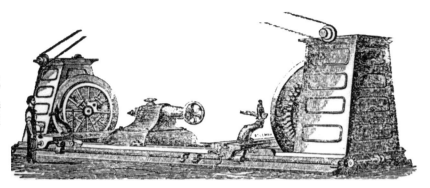

LEACH, SHEPARD, Easton, MA

Primarily a foundry, the firm made, in 1814, "lathes and cutting engines."

LEBLOND, R.K., Cincinnati, OH, later
LEBLOND MACHINE TOOL CO., R.K., Cincinnati, OH

Founded in 1887 by Richard K. LeBlond (1864-1953) to make gages and small tools. In 1891, it began making 16" engine lathes on contract for LODGE & DAVIS MACHINE TOOL CO. In 1896, the Lodge & Davis contract ended and LeBlond began making 12", 14" and 16" engine lathes under his own mame.

The firm incorporated as the R.K. LEBLOND MACHINE TOOL CO. in 1898 with a capital of $50,000. 18" swing engine lathes were added in 1899 and a line of milling machines in 1900.

Lathe production in 1901 expanded to include 20" (Fig.1) and 24" (Fig.2) engine lathes. Engine lathes with quick change feed gear boxes (Fig.3) were introduced in 1904. 1905 production included 18" roughing lathes (Fig.4) with heavy carriages and tool posts for roughing cuts, 16" plain turret lathes (Fig.5), 31" triple geared turret lathes (Fig.6), and 25" combination turret lathes (Fig.7).

1908 production included 14" toolmakers' lathes (Fig.8), double manufacturing lathes (Fig.9), and a newly introduced 21" turret lathe with variable speed electric motor drive (Fig.10). A line of heavy duty "Automobile" lathes (Fig.11) in 16", 18" and 20" swings and equipped with quick change feed gear boxes was introduced in 1909. *(Illustrations continued on next page.)*

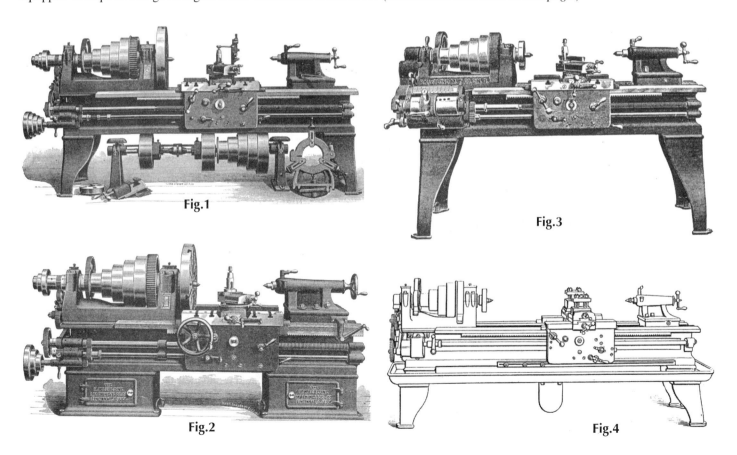

Fig.1

Fig.3

Fig.2

Fig.4

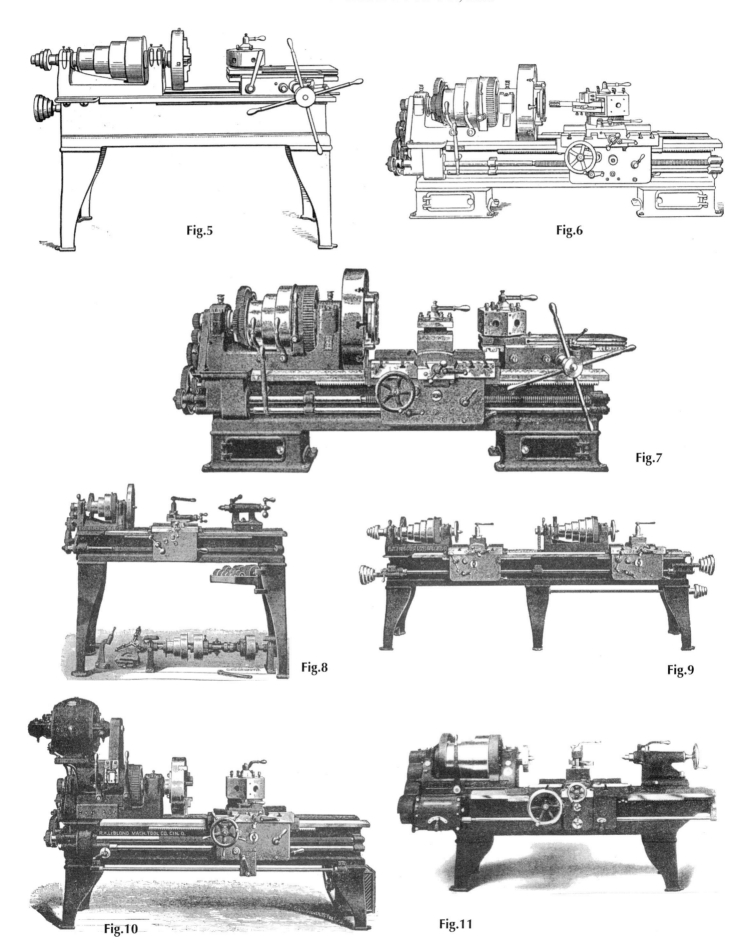

Fig.5

Fig.6

Fig.7

Fig.8

Fig.9

Fig.10

Fig.11

LEONARD & CLARK, New York, NY

Makers, in 1860-1861, of "all sizes of engines lathes from $325 to $1900."

LIBERTY MFG. CO., Liberty, IN

Formed in 1892 to build wire fence machines. Lathe production began in 1894 when Peter Shellenback consolidated his SHELLENBACK MACHINE TOOL CO. with the Liberty Mfg. Co., and continued until the company failed in 1897. Total assets in 1897 were only $23,000.

LINCOLN & CO., Hartford, CT

See PHOENIX IRON WORKS

LLOYD-BOOTH CO., Youngstown, OH

A large maker of a variety of steel mill machinery, the firm made a line of roll lathes designed for machining custom rolls used in steel mill rolling lines. In 1889 the firm introduced a new design, a 22' bed, roll lathe which could handle rolls up to 30" in diameter. Note the extreme reduction ratio (163 to 1) apparent in the illustration below.

LODGE, BARKER & CO., Cincinnati, OH

A partnership of William Lodge (1848-1917) and William Barker (1853-1915) formed January 1, 1880. Both Lodge and Barker had previously worked for the JOHN STEPTOE CO. The firm was reorganized as LODGE, DAVIS & CO. when Charles Davis replaced Barker in January, 1886.

Products included 18" engine lathes (Fig.1) introduced in 1880, 15" turret lathes (Fig.2) introduced in 1881, 13" turret lathes (Fig.3) introduced in 1882, and FOX monitor lathes introduced in 1883 (Fig.4).

Later production included improved engine lathes (Fig.5), square arbor FOX lathes (Fig.6), and improved 13" turret lathes (Fig.7) all introduced in 1884. 19" chucking lathes (Fig.8), 60" gap chucking lathes (Fig.9), and 16" plain turret lathes (Fig.10) were offered in 1885.
(continued next two pages)

Fig.1

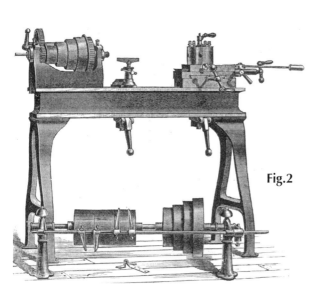

Fig.2

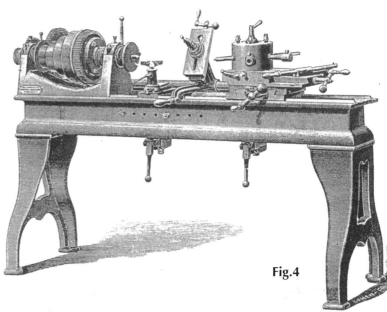

Fig.4

NEW "FOX" MONITOR LATHE.

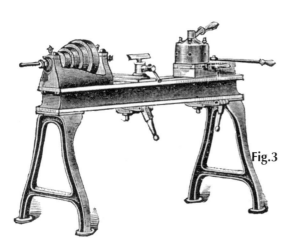

Fig.3

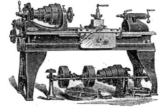

LODGE, BARKER & CO., Cincinnati, Ohio,
MANUFACTURERS OF
ENGINE LATHES

from 6 to 25-foot Bed, Turret Lathes, Hand Fox Lathes, Valve Milling Machines, Slide Rests, Box Chucks, etc., and Dealers in Machinists' Tools.

Lathes of various sizes and lengths for immediate delivery.

N. W. COR. SIXTH ST. AND EGGLESTON AVE.

Fig.5

LODGE, BARKER & CO.,
200 to 210 Eggleston Ave.,
CINCINNATI, OHIO.

These Lathes are fitted with Square Arbors in the most thorough manner, and constructed so that the wear on the Square Spindle may be taken up, keeping the spindle perfectly central, insuring great solidity during the whole life of the Lathe. We manufacture these Lathes either with or without Chasing Apparatus, and fit them with Turret Head when so ordered.

It will pay you to correspond with us.

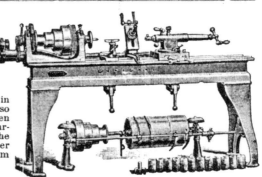

Fig.6

Fig.7

Fig.8

Fig.9

Fig.10

LODGE, DAVIS & CO., Cincinnati, OH, later
LODGE & DAVIS MACHINE TOOL CO., Cincinnati, OH

A partnership of William Lodge (1848-1817) and Charles Davis (1853-1903) formed in January, 1886, as a reorganization of LODGE, BARKER & CO. In 1889, the firm became a stock company, the LODGE & DAVIS MACHINE TOOL CO. Lodge left the firm in March, 1892, to found the OHIO MACHINE TOOL WORKS. Davis, who became president when Lodge departed, reorganized as the DAVIS & EGAN MACHINE TOOL CO. September 1, 1896, when Thomas P. Egan bought an interest.

Henry Dreses (1854-1930), who had joined the firm in 1883, was chief designer by 1892, serving until 1896 when he left to form DRESES, MUELLER & CO.

Products offered in 1888 included 21" turret chucking lathes (Fig.1), IMPERIAL 17" manufacturers' lathes (Fig.2), heavy engine lathes from 17" to 30" (Fig.3), 38" engine lathes (Fig.4), and FOX monitor lathes (Fig.5). *(continued next three pages)*

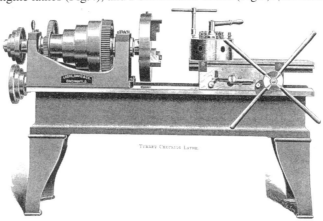

Fig.1

93

Combination lathes with turret on the shears (Fig.6) or on the carriage (Fig.7), new 16" tool room lathes (Fig.8) with Slate taper attachment, and 24" manufacturers' lathes were introduced in 1891.

1892 production included a new 36" pulley lathe (Fig.9) and new heavy turret lathe (Fig.10). New cabinet style, 20" turret lathes (Fig.11), and 36" triple geared engine lathes (Fig.12) were introduced in 1893.

In 1894, the firm introduced one of the first electric motor driven lathes (Fig.13), with a variable speed motor mounted in place of the cone pulley. Speed and direction were controlled by a rod connected to a control box mounted under the machine.

New products introduced in 1895 included the STANDARD engine lathe (Fig.14) in 14" swing only, screw machines with the Parkhurst wire feed (Fig.15), and a redesigned line of engine lathes from 20" swing (Fig.16) to 48" swing .

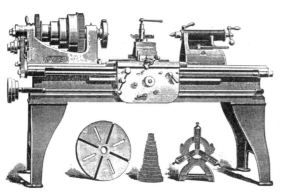

Fig.2

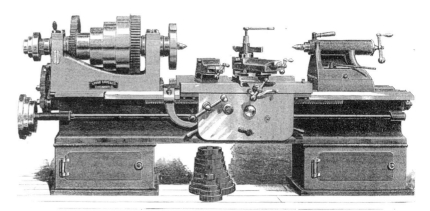

New Heavy Lathe.

Fig.3

Fig.4

Fig.5

Turret on Shear.

Fig.6

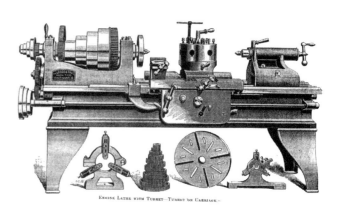

Engine Lathe with Turret—Turret on Carriage.

Fig.7

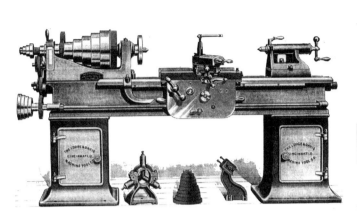

Fig.8

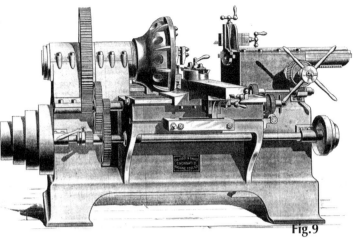

Fig.9

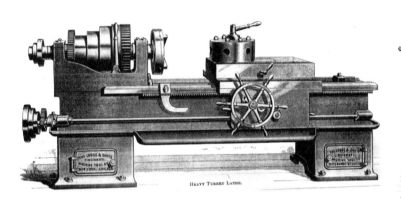

Fig.10

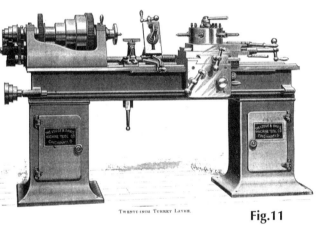

Fig.11

Fig.12

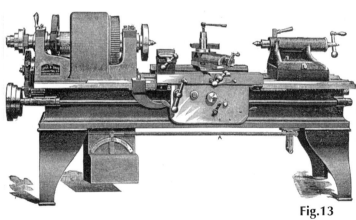

Fig.13

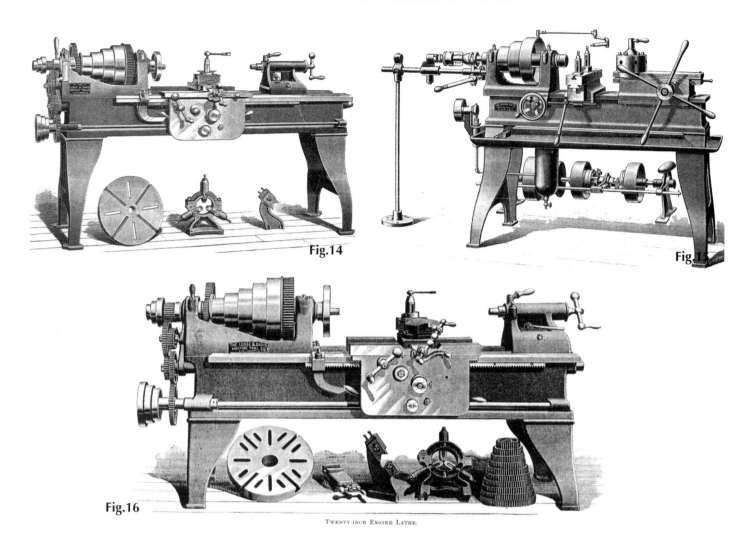

Fig.14

Fig.15

Fig.16

TWENTY-INCH ENGINE LATHE.

LODGE & SHIPLEY MACHINE TOOL CO., Cincinnati, OH

A partnership of William Lodge (1848-1917) and Murray Shipley (1865-1929), formed August 1, 1892, as a reorganization of the OHIO MACHINE TOOL WORKS. Lodge served as president and general manager until his death in 1917. Shipley served as vice president and secretary until selling out to the Lodge estate in 1917.

Products in 1893 included 22" turret chucking lathes (Fig.1), 24" turret chucking lathes (Fig.2), 27" turret lathes (Fig.3), 30" pulley lathes (Fig.4), 60" pulley lathes (Fig.5), 30" heavy lathes "for steam engine makers" (Fig.6), and 30" lathes, with power feed tail stock, for making large gear blanks (Fig.7).

In 1895, the firm introduced an 18" engine lathe with their first attempt at a quick change feed gear box (Fig.8). Two years later a 14" model with an improved quick change feed gear box (Fig.9) was introduced. *(continued next three pages)*

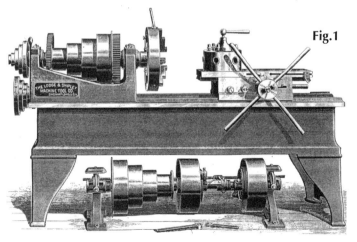

Fig.1

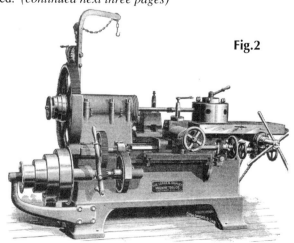

Fig.2

Larger engine lathes with quick change gear feed boxes were available by 1900, including 24" (Fig.10) and 36" models. A "High Speed" lathe with quick change feed gear box and all geared head, for use with the new high speed steel cutting tools, was introduced in 1903 (Fig.11). In 1904 a 16" electric motor-driven lathe (Fig.12), equipped with a two-speed motor and six gear changes, was introduced

A portable 16" lathe, mounted on wheels (Fig.13) was introduced in 1908. It was intended for use in locomotive repair shops and the assembly floor of shops making heavy machinery.

The MARVEL lathe, designed for machining bar stock (Fig.14) and furnished with quick-change gear boxes for both feed and spindle was introduced in 1909. Two sizes were offered; 2½" x 36" and 4" x 48".

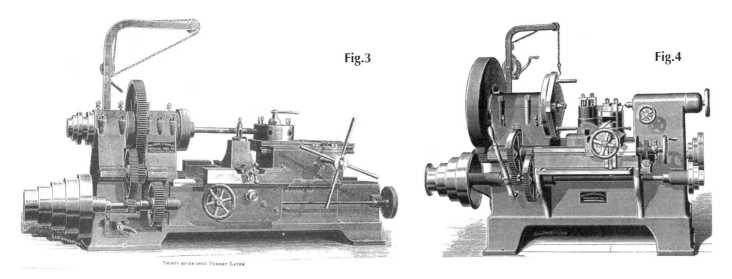

Fig.3 — Thirty-seven-inch Turret Lathe.

Fig.4

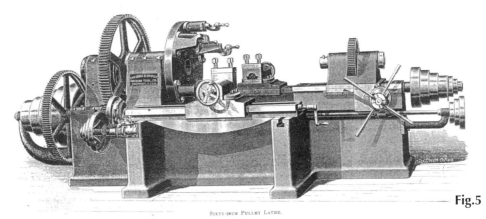

Fig.5 — Sixty-inch Pulley Lathe.

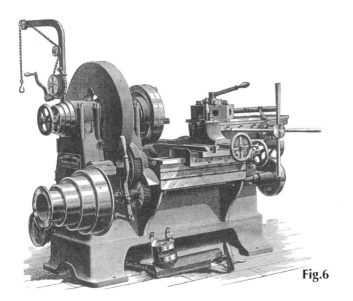

Fig.6

Fig.7

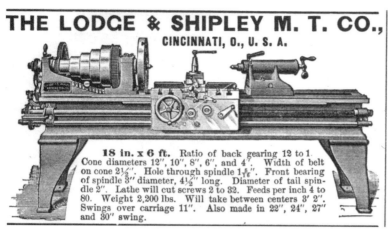

THE LODGE & SHIPLEY M. T. CO.,
CINCINNATI, O., U. S. A.

18 in. x 6 ft. Ratio of back gearing 12 to 1. Cone diameters 12", 10", 8", 6", and 4". Width of belt on cone 2½". Hole through spindle 1 5/16". Front bearing of spindle 3" diameter, 4½" long. Diameter of tail spindle 2". Lathe will cut screws 2 to 32. Feeds per inch 4 to 80. Weight 2,200 lbs. Will take between centers 3' 2". Swings over carriage 11". Also made in 22", 24", 27" and 30" swing.

Fig.8

Fig.9

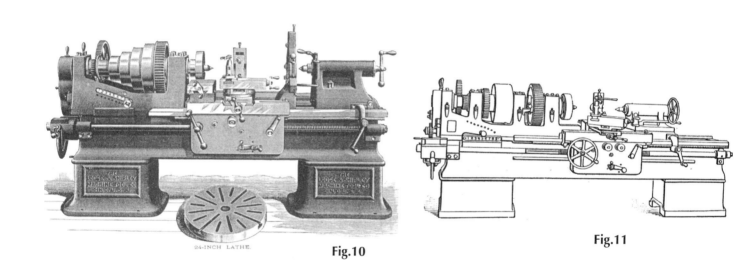

24-INCH LATHE.

Fig.10

Fig.11

Fig.12

98

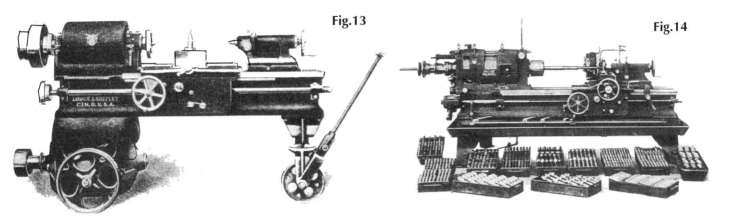

Fig.13

Fig.14

LOVELL, F.S., Fitchburg, MA

Maker, in 1883, of engine lathes, hand lathes, chucks and other machinery. The firm was burned out in 1894.

LOWELL MACHINE SHOP, Lowell, MA

Formed in January, 1845, the company was primarily a maker of textile machinery. It also made a wide variety of machine tools (Fig.1), most of which were designed by William B. Bement (1817-1897).

Lathe production in 1851 included large chucking lathes (Fig.2), gap lathes (Fig.3), and engine lathes (Fig.4) as illustrated in the 1851 book Metal-Workers Assistant. Lathes offered in its January, 1863, catalog included engine lathes up to 50" swing (Fig.5) weighing 11,000 pounds and priced at $2,310. The firm operated until 1897, but the manufacture of machine tools was discontinued in 1867.

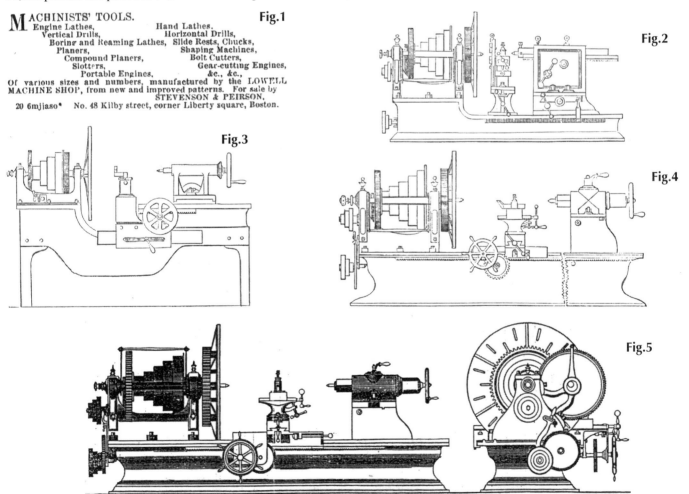

MACHINISTS' TOOLS.
Engine Lathes,   Hand Lathes.
   Vertical Drills,   Horizontal Drills,
      Boring and Reaming Lathes, Slide Rests, Chucks,
         Planers,   Shaping Machines,
            Compound Planers,   Bolt Cutters,
               Slotters,   Gear-cutting Engines,
                  Portable Engines,   &c., &c.,
Of various sizes and numbers, manufactured by the LOWELL
MACHINE SHOP, from new and improved patterns. For sale by
                     STEVENSON & PEIRSON,
20 6mjiaso*   No. 48 Kilby street, corner Liberty square, Boston.

Fig.1

Fig.2

Fig.3

Fig.4

Fig.5

MANN, CHARLES A., Providence, RI

Maker, c1885-1905, of small lathes "for foot or other power," designed so that a countershaft could easily be put in place of the foot-power. Models included an 11" foot lathe (Fig.1) and a 10" speed lathe (Fig.2). An optional slide rest (Fig.3) was offered as an accessory for the speed lathe.

SCREW CUTTING ENGINE LATHE. **Fig.1**

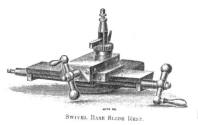

SWIVEL BASE SLIDE REST. **Fig.3**

Fig.2

MANSFIELD, WALLACE H., New Haven, CT

Maker, beginning in 1895, of 10" foot power engine lathes "adapted for milling." The milling feature consisted of a sliding table on the tool carriage, which was fed automatically and elevated by a screw. *(see right)*

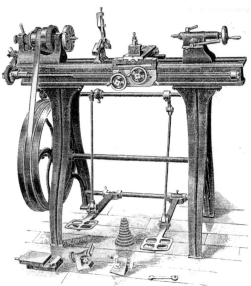

A LATHE ADAPTED FOR MILLING.

MARSHALL, BEMENT & COLBY, Philadelphia, PA

A partnership of Elijah D. Marshall, William B. Bement (1817-1897) and Gilbert A. Colby, formed in 1851 to make large machine tools. Bement had been a machine designer for the LOWELL MACHINE SHOP from 1845 to 1851. The firm reorganized as BEMENT, COLBY, DOUGHERTY & CO. when James Dougherty replaced Marshall in 1853.

MARVEL & CO., C.M., Lowell, MA

Founded c1835 by Caleb M. Marvel to make textile machinery and "machine tools of every description" including a variety of lathes.

MASON MACHINE WORKS, Taunton, MA

Operated by William Mason c1850-1870. Maker of locomotives, textile machinery, and machine tools, including lathes.

McCABE LATHE & MACHINERY CO., J.J., New York, NY

Formed in 1890 by J.J. McCabe (?-1919) who took over the machinery sales business of the E.P. BULLARD CO. McCabe had been long associated with Bullard, beginning as the son of Bullard's milkman and becoming something of a foster son.

About 1895, McCabe introduced a unique, double spindle lathe of his own design. Early production of the lathe (Fig.1) offered a swing of 24" on the main spindle and 38" on the secondary spindle. Later production (Fig.2) was of heavier construction and offered swings of 28"/44" and 28"/48". The lathe was made through World War I.

Fig.1

Double Spindle Lathe, 26-44 inch Swing.

Fig.2

McCONNELL, J.E., Iowa City, IA

Maker, in 1881, of 24"x 20' engine lathes and 26"x 24"x 8' planers.

McDOWELL, STOCKER & CO., Chicago, IL

A large machinery dealer, the firm introduced its brand name ILLINOIS lathe in 1907. Probably made for them under contract, the machine was offered in 14" swing only and was "intended to meet the needs of general service in shops requiring a plain, substantial machine." In other words, a low price machine. *(see right)*

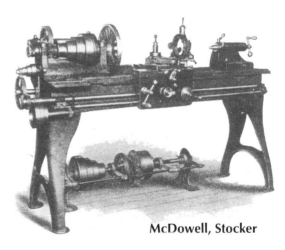

McDowell, Stocker

McFARLAN & NOTTINGHAM, Cincinnati, OH

A partnership of Thomas McFarlan and Henry E. Nottingham, formed in 1875 when McFarlan left the partnership of STEPTOE, McFARLAN & CO. The firm made lathes and drilling machines through 1885 or later.

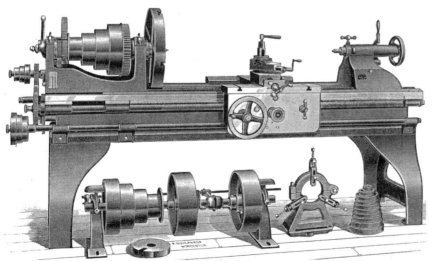

McMAHON & CARVER, Worcester, MA, later,
McMAHON & CO., Worcester, MA

Formed about 1882 as a partnership of Michael F. McMahon and Thomas F. Carver. By 1888 the firm had been reorganized as McMAHON & CO. and continued to make 20" engine lathes such as shown at left.

MERIDEN MACHINE TOOL CO., Meriden, CT

Formed in 1889 by H. Wales Lines, Walter Cheney and Robert L. Peck. Early products were mostly forming lathes (Fig.1), including a turret model (Fig.2), and a bench model (Fig.3).

In 1893, the firm introduced turret lathes (Fig.4) offered in 12" and 18" swings. A heavier duty model with 20" swing (Fig.5) was introduced in 1909. Note the odd brace from the back of the turret slide to the top of the turret. The company appears to have failed about 1927.

Fig.1

A NEW FORMING LATHE.

Fig.2

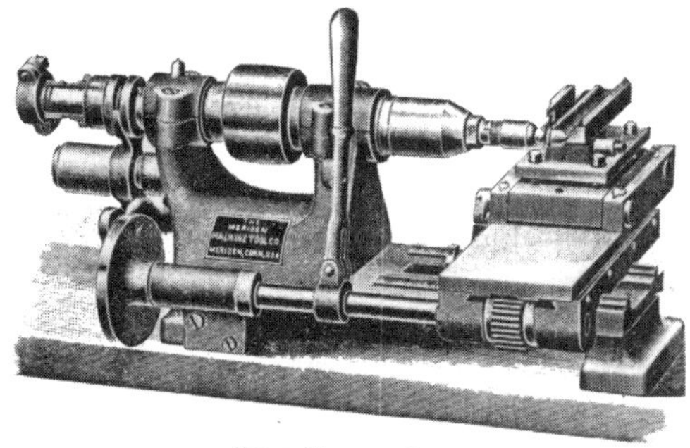

Fig.3

BENCH FORMING LATHE.

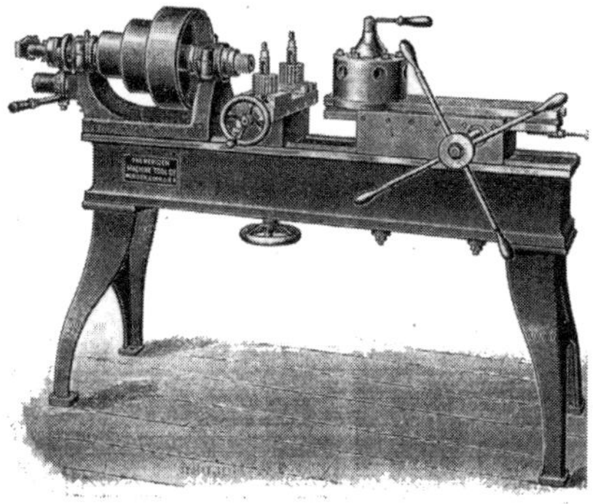

Fig.4

IMPROVED TURRET LATHE.

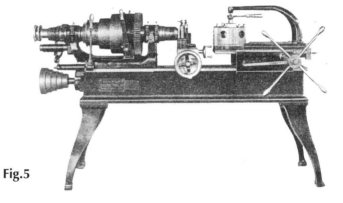

Fig.5

MIAMI VALLEY MACHINE TOOL CO., Dayton, OH

Founded by Samuel D. Conover (1843-1912) in 1900. The firm was reorganized as the CONOVER-OVERCAMP MACHINE & TOOL CO. in 1912.

Early products included 13" engine lathes and stud lathes. A 15" engine lathe, identical to the 13" lathe except for size, was introduced in 1909.

(see left)

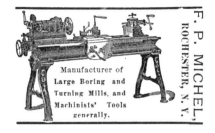

MICHEL, F.P., Rochester, NY

Engine lathe maker operating c1877-1883. He also made large vertical boring and turning mills. *(see right)*

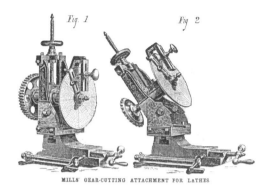

MILLS' GEAR-CUTTING ATTACHMENT FOR LATHES

MICHIGAN MFG. CO., Kalamazoo, MI

Maker, in 1876, of MILL'S patent gear cutting attachment for lathes. It was 24" in height with a 12" index plate with 36 circles of holes. The attachment is shown at left, arranged for cutting spur gears (Fig.1) and bevel gears (Fig.2).

MICHIGAN TOOL WORKS, Grand Rapids, MI

Formed in 1881 by Thomas Farmer, Jr. to make engine lathes, including an 18" swing (Fig.1) introduced in 1882. It was equipped with a newly designed adjustable tool post (Fig.2) also introduced in 1882. The firm operated into the 1890's.

Fig.1

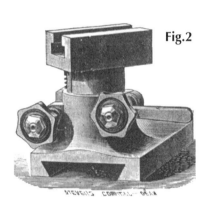

Fig.2

MILLBURY MACHINE CO., Millbury, MA

Founded about 1863 by E.J. Humpreys (1838-1907) and John Humpreys. Maker of engine lathes, drilling lathes and upright drills. John Humpreys' patent of November 3, 1868, for a feed gear change system for engine lathes was one of the early designs for quick change feed gearing.

MILWAUKEE MACHINE TOOL CO.,Milwaukee, WI

Formed in 1902 by John J. Hay, Edwin Cheshire, and Charles E. Search. Search and Cheshire were the developers of a large turret lathe, jointly patented August 18, 1903; Hay had been secretary and treasurer of the R.K. LeBLOND MACHINE TOOL CO.

The turret lathe shown at right was the firm's sole product. Weighing 11,000 lbs., it was made with a 4½" spindle hole, 28" swing, and independent power feeds to carriage and turret.

In 1904, the firm was bought out by the NILES-BEMENT-POND CO., probably to obtain the patents, drawings and patterns for the large turret lathe. Production was immediately moved to the POND MACHINE TOOL CO. division of NILES-BEMENT-POND CO.

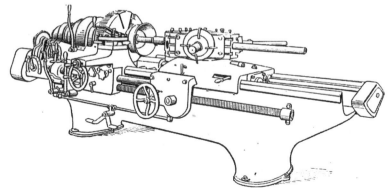

MILWAUKEE MACHINE TOOL CO., Milwaukee, WI

Formed in 1907 with a capital of $20,000 to make "engine lathes in 16" swing only" (Fig.1). An improved 16" model, with friction gear drive for the feed, was introduced in 1909. A new design lathe (Fig.2) was introduced in 1910 and offered in swings from 16" to 20".

In 1913 the company was bought by Kearney & Trecker Co., which continued to operate it until 1915 or later.

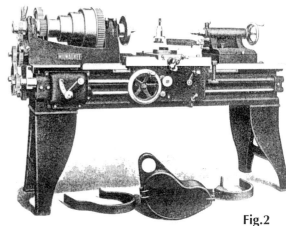

Fig.1

Fig.2

MOLINE TOOL CO., Moline, IL

Formed March 4, 1901, by Wilson P. Hunt (1873-1948) and George Ahrens when they bought and reorganized the Moline Pattern & Machine Works. The firm was incorporated in 1903 with Hunt as general manager. Hunt later served as president from 1910 to 1929.

Early products included speed lathes, gang drills, bolt cutters, etc. Gang drills, later named HOLE HOG drills, became its primary product.

In 1905, the firm introduced a turret lathe with a 3¾" hole through the spindle, a four position turret and two cross slides. As illustrated below, the machine featured a then unique design in which the bed, cast in hollow box form and integral with the headstock, slanted to the rear "so the chips slide off into the pan at the rear." The bed construction and slant design were far advanced for 1905.

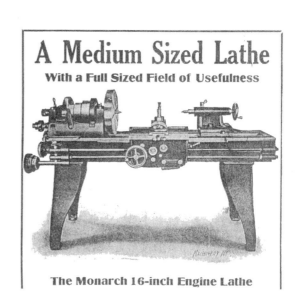

MONARCH MACHINE CO., Sidney, OH

Formed in 1909 by Ignatius H. Thedieck (1855-1926) when he took control of the A.P. WAGNER CO., moved it to Sidney and renamed it. In 1916, the company was reorganized as the Monarch Machine Tool Co. Products included 16" engine lathes such as shown at right.

A Medium Sized Lathe

With a Full Sized Field of Usefulness

The Monarch 16-inch Engine Lathe

MORRIS FOUNDRY CO., JOHN B., Cincinnati, OH, later
MORRIS MACHINE TOOL CO., JOHN B., Cincinnati, OH

Founded by John B. Morris in 1891, the firm began making machine tools when it bought the radial drill business of Roos & Mill about 1906.

Lathe production began in 1908 with a 16" geared head and feed lathe (Fig.1) designed by William L. Schellenbach for use with the new high speed steel cutting tools. In 1909 a cone head version (Fig.2), also designed by Schellenbach, was offered in 14", 16" and 18" sizes. The company reorganized as the JOHN B. MORRIS MACHINE TOOL CO. in 1910.

Fig.1

Fig. 1. Schellenbach Geared Head and Feed 16-inch Lathe.

Fig.2

MOSELEY & CO., H.N., Elgin, IL, later
MOSELEY LATHE CO., Elgin, IL

Formed by Horace N. Moseley about 1885. Moseley was proprietor until the firm failed in 1896 and incorporated as the MOSELEY LATHE CO. Operation continued until at least 1906.

Products included small precision lathes and other machinery for the Elgin watch industry as shown in the 1900 advertisement at right.

Our Counters, with Self-Oiling Pulleys and Boxes, excel them all.
ORIGINATORS, DESIGNERS AND MANUFACTURERS OF THE
American Hollow Spindle Bench Lathe & Split Self-Centering Chucks
Indispensable for the Watchmaker, the Toolmaker and the Manufacturer.
When interested write **MOSELEY LATHE CO.**, Elgin, Ill., U. S. A.
Catalog and Circulars mailed to any address.

MULLER MACHINE TOOL CO., Cincinnati, OH

Founded in 1886 by Edward A. Muller (1867-?) who had worked for SEBASTIAN, MAY & CO. Muller, who made his lathes in space rented inside the BRADFORD MILL CO. factory, merged with Bradford in 1890, staying on as superintendent until leaving in 1892 to join LODGE & DAVIS.

Production was limited to 16" (Fig.1) engine lathes introduced in 1886 and 17" (Fig.2) engine lathes introduced in 1888.

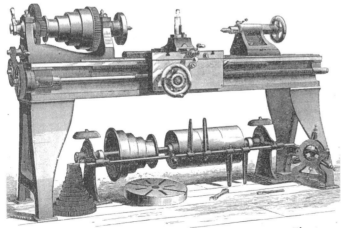

16-INCH ENGINE LATHE.   **Fig.1**

Fig.2

MUNZER, WILLIAM, New York, NY

Maker of engine lathes and steam engines from c1870 until his death in 1885.

NARRAGANSETT MACHINE CO., Providence, RI

Formed about 1882 to make light machine tools and gymnasium equipment. Lathe offerings included an 8" swing foot lathe for amateurs (Fig.1) that was also made in a bench model (Fig.2).

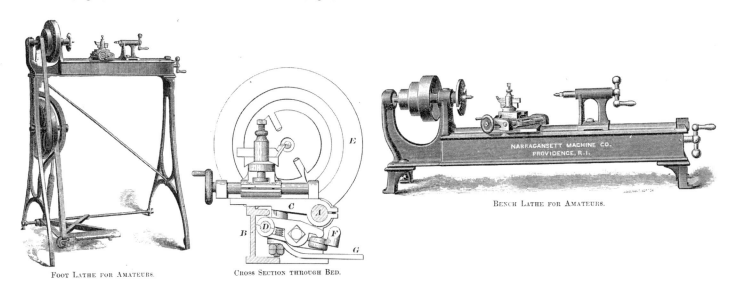

FOOT LATHE FOR AMATEURS.

CROSS SECTION THROUGH BED.

BENCH LATHE FOR AMATEURS.

NASH, SYLVESTER, Springfield, MA

An employee of the Springfield Armory, Nash invented a lathe for turning musket barrels that he patented April 11, 1818. Nash probably did not make the machines, but sold the rights to the U.S. Government for $500.

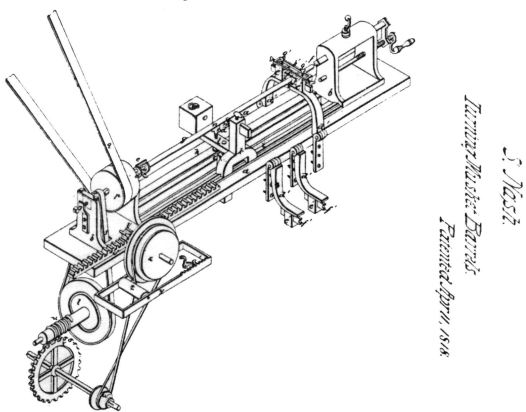

NASHUA MFG. CO., Nashua, NH
Founded in 1824 to make a variety of machinery, including engine lathes. Ira Gay was superintendent.

NEW HAVEN MFG. CO., New Haven, CT
Founded in 1850 by Asahel Pierpont who had moved to New Haven from Springfield, MA. Very early products are unknown, but by 1860 the firm offered lathes, planers, and drilling machines.

In 1882, the firm's production had reached a value of $300,000, indicating a large firm for the time. R.A. Brown was president, but the firm was operated by Leslie Moulthrop, secretary, and Alexander Thayer, superintendent. Thayer had previously been associated with THAYER, HOUGHTON & CO. and the NEW YORK STEAM ENGINE CO.

Lathes offered in 1884-1886 included 60" pulley lathes (Fig.1), 18" engine lathes (Fig.2), 22" engine lathes (Fig.3), 26" engine lathes, 30" engine lathes, 36" engine lathes (Fig.4), horizontal boring lathes (Fig.5), and 25" pattern makers lathes (Fig.6). Three tool slide rests for turning shafting were offered by 1887.

About 1890, Oscar E. Perrigo (?-1923) was put in charge of machine design. Serving until he moved to PRATT & WHITNEY CO. in 1917, Perrigo developed a number of lathes, including 21" engine lathes (Fig.7) with a parabolic bed for extra rigidity, patented in 1893. 1896-1898 products included screw cutting engine lathes in several sizes (Fig.8) and triple geared engine lathes up to 60" (Fig.9).

Engine lathes with Joseph Judd design quick-change feed gear boxes, including a 36" size (Fig.10), were introduced in 1906, followed by a Perrigo design offered on 21" (Fig.11) to 32" lathes in 1907. *(Illustrations continued on next two pages.)*

Fig.1

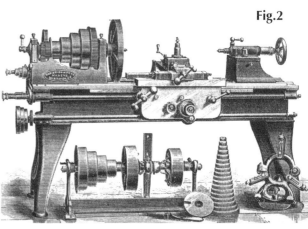

Fig.2

Fig.3

Fig.4

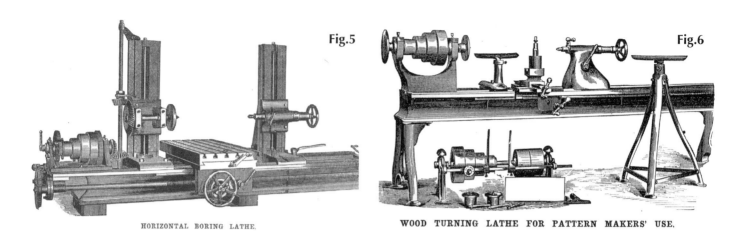

Fig.5

HORIZONTAL BORING LATHE.

Fig.6

WOOD TURNING LATHE FOR PATTERN MAKERS' USE.

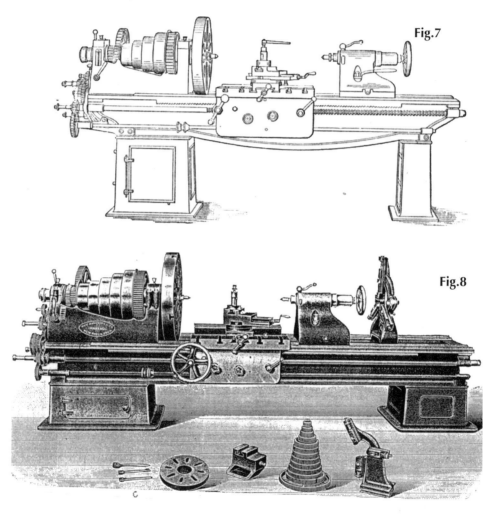

Fig.7

Fig.8

Fig.9

Fig.10

Fig.11

21-inch Screw
Cutting Lathe

NEW YORK STEAM ENGINE WORKS, New York, NY and Worcester, MA

Formed about 1860 to make steam engines, the firm began the manufacture of lathes and other machine tools in 1862, when it purchased the assets of THAYER, HOUGHTON & CO. Production of the Thayer, Houghton line of lathes (Fig.1) in several sizes from 14" to 76" continued under the management of Alexander Thayer (1812-1895).

Thayer left in 1864 to join the NEW HAVEN MFG. CO. Alfred B. Couch (1829-1888) was then appointed superintendent and general manager. An improved line of Couch designed lathes was introduced by 1866. Couch left in 1871 to join WM. B. BEMENT & SON as a machine designer. The Worcester factory was closed in 1871 and production moved to its Passaic, NJ, factory. Machine tools, including 20" engine lathes advertised in 1874 (Fig.2), were produced until the factory closed in 1877.

Fig.1

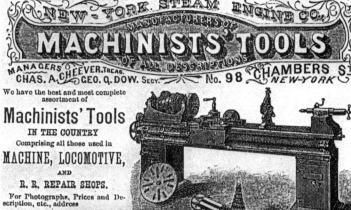

Fig.2

NEWARK MACHINE TOOL WORKS, Newark, NJ

Formed in 1886 by Henry B. Binsse, as the successor to the business of GEORGE A. OHL & CO. Maker of 32" and 42" engine lathes, slotters, drilling and boring machines 1886-1888.

About 1889 the firm began to specialize in horizontal drilling and boring machines. In 1901 the company became the Binsse Machine Co.

NICHOLS, S.H., Baldwinsville, NY

Maker of 32" x 12' engine lathes in 1865.

NICHOLSON & WATERMAN, Providence, RI

A partnership of Stephen Nicholson and his brother-in-law Stephen Waterman formed in 1887. Products included engine lathes such as shown below and horizontal drilling machines. Nicholson was the son of William T. Nicholson, founder of the Nicholson File Co. Short lived, the firm appears to have gone out of business about 1892.

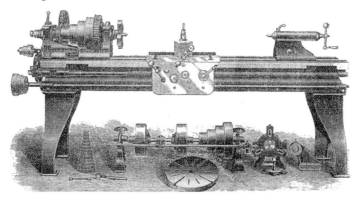

NILES & CO., Cincinnati, OH, later
NILES TOOL WORKS, Hamilton, OH

A partnership of James Niles (1809-1881) and his brother Johnathon Niles (1804-1878) formed in 1845. Early products included steam engines and locomotives. The brothers began making machine tools about 1859 and by 1868 offered engine lathes from 14" to 60" swing. In 1869, the brothers sold out to Alexander Gordon (1839-1910), George A. Gray, Jr. (1839-1905) and James W. Gaff. The partnership of GAFF, GORDON & GRAY (Fig.1, right) operated the company as the NILES TOOL WORKS. The new firm specialized in large machine tools for the railroad industry.

Niles Tool Works,
CINCINNATI, OHIO.
MACHINISTS' TOOLS OF THE BEST
descriptio·, at reasonable prices.
Gaff, Gray & Gordon
Have purchased the entire interest of the
NILES WORKS,
In this branch of their business, and will continue the
manufacture of
MACHINISTS' TOOLS,
with increased facilities.
IRON-WORKING MACHINERY
is a SPECIALTY with us.

The factory was moved to Hamilton, OH, in 1873 and the firm incorporated in 1874. Gray left the firm in 1877 to form G.A. GRAY, JR. & CO. Gaff died in 1879 and his son, James W. Gaff, Jr., succeeded his father as president. George T. Reiss (1849-1915) was appointed chief engineer in 1879 and was responsible for machine design for Niles and, later, Niles-Bement-Pond, until his death in 1915.

Alexander Gordon became president when the firm was reorganized in 1892, serving until August 15, 1899, when the NILES TOOL WORKS merged with BEMENT, MILES & CO. and the POND MACHINE TOOL CO. to form the NILES-BEMENT-POND CO. Niles continued operation as a division of the NILES-BEMENT-POND CO.

Products included double axle lathes (Fig.2) in 1873, and large, 2" screw machines/turret lathes (Fig.3) introduced in 1883. 1884 offerings included improved double axle lathes (Fig.4), 26" engine lathes (Fig.5), 30" and 36" engine lathes, 42" engine lathes (Fig.6), 42", 54" and 60" (Fig.7) engine lathes, 79", 84" and 90" driving wheel lathes (Fig.8), and car wheel lathes (Fig.9). A new special pulley turning lathe (Fig.10) was introduced in 1884. *(continued on next 4 pages)*

Fig.2

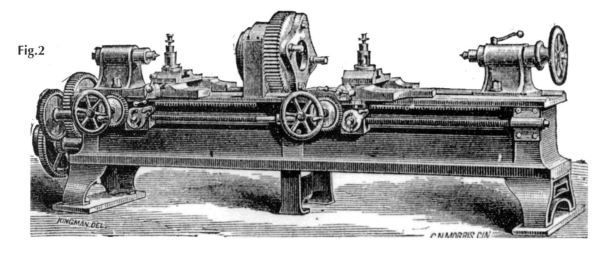

By 1891 Niles offered improved screw machines/turret lathes in 1" No.2 (Fig.11) and 1½" No.3 sizes. Production in 1893 included engine lathes in 22", 24", 28", 30", 32", 36", 42", 48" (Fig.12), 54", 60", and 72" swings; and forge lathes in 38", 50", 60"(Fig.13), 72", 84", and 90" (Fig.14), swings. New products in 1895 included a 62", double head engine lathe (Fig.15) with two complete lathes mounted in a single 63' bed.

A new design turret lathe/screw machine (Fig.16) was introduced in 1896. Made in 2"x 24" size, it was claimed to "have all the advantages of their screw machines, combined with those of any flat turret lathe."

By 1900 turret lathes and all but the largest engine lathes had been discontinued. The Niles 1903 catalog offered driving wheel lathes (Fig.17), 70" forge lathes, improved single axle lathes (Fig.18) and double axle lathes (Fig.19), and car-wheel lathes (Fig.20).

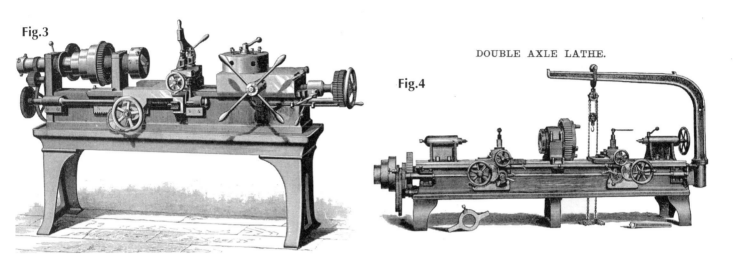

Fig.3

DOUBLE AXLE LATHE.

Fig.4

26 INCH ENGINE LATHE.

Fig.5

42 INCH LATHE.

Fig.6

60, 54, AND 42 INCH SWING ENGINE LATHES.

Fig.7

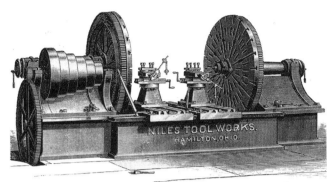

Fig.8

DOUBLE-HEAD DRIVING WHEEL LATHE.

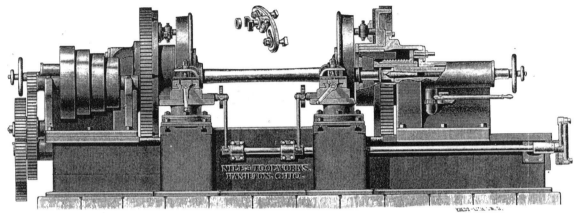

Fig.9

NILES CAR-WHEEL-LATHE FOR TURNING STEEL-TIRED WHEELS.

NILES' SPECIAL PULLEY TURNING LATHE.

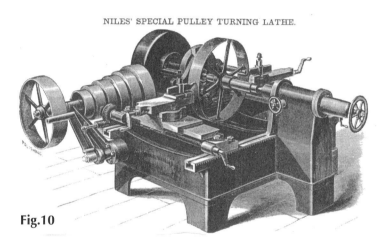

Fig.10

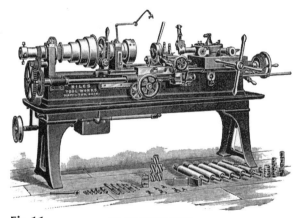

Fig.11

NO. 2 SCREW MACHINE

Fig.12

60-INCH HEAVY FORGE LATHE.

Fig.13

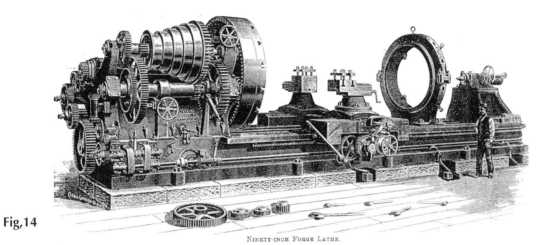

Fig,14

NINETY-INCH FORGE LATHE.

Fig.15   THE NILES SIXTY-TWO INCH DOUBLE HEAD LATHE.

Fig.16

Fig.17

Fig.18

Fig.19

Fig.20

NORTON, W.P., Bristol, CT, later
NORTON & JONES MACHINE TOOL WORKS, Plainville, CT

Founded by Wendell P. Norton (1861-?) in 1889 to make lathes and small drilling machines. In 1890, the firm reorganized as the NORTON & JONES MACHINE TOOL WORKS and moved to Plainville, CT. The company closed in 1892 when Norton returned to the HENDEY MACHINE CO.

OHIO MACHINE TOOL WORKS, Cincinnati, OH

Founded by William Lodge (1848-1917) March 1, 1892, soon after leaving the LODGE & DAVIS MACHINE TOOL CO. Short-lived, the firm was reorganized as the LODGE & SHIPLEY MACHINE TOOL CO. August 1, 1892. The sole product was a new design of pulley lathe, offered in five sizes from 20" to 60".

A New Machine Tool.

OHL & CO., G.A., Newark, NJ

Founded by George A. Ohl (1837-1922) about 1879 to make engine lathes and FOX lathes. The firm was active until Ohl's retirement in 1898. Products included long bed engine lathes such as that shown below.

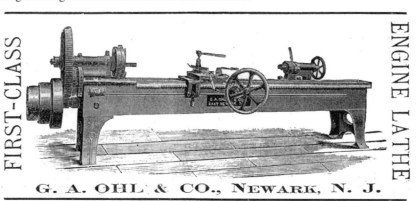

G. A. OHL & CO., NEWARK, N. J.

OSGOOD, ISAAC, Amesbury and Holyoke, MA

Born Amesbury, MA, in 1814, Osgood was a maker of engine lathes c1850-1860. He worked for Remington Arms Co. during the Civil War, then returned to Amesbury, MA, where he made OSGOOD oil-grooving lathes into the 20th century.

PALMER, J.C., Philadelphia, PA

Maker, beginning in 1886, of Palmer's gear cutting attachment for lathes *(right)*. Designed to be mounted in the tool carriage, it had a vertical adjustment of 4" and was furnished with two index plates. The same device was sold by the SEBASTIAN LATHE CO. as late as 1898.

GEAR-CUTTING ATTACHMENT.

PARKER & KNIGHT CO., Baltimore, MD

Formed in 1891 by John H. Parker and F.E. Knight with a capital of $25,000. Maker of 17", heavy duty, engine lathes (Fig.). The firm also offered the PARKER lathe tool holder (Fig.) developed in 1891.

Fig.1

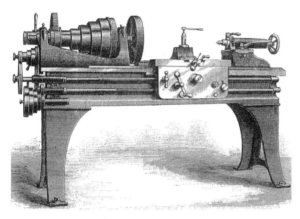

SCREW CUTTING ENGINE LATHE.

Fig.2

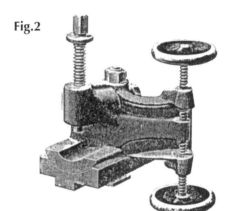

PARKER'S ADJUSTABLE LATHE TOOL HOLDER.

PAWTUCKET MFG. CO., Pawtucket, RI

Formed about 1890 by George H. Webb to manufacture bolt and nut making machinery. Webb served as general manager and treasurer until his death in 1920. In 1898, the firm introduced the Webb patent manufacturing lathe, shown at right.

PEARSON & PHELPS, Chicago, IL, later
PEARSON MACHINE CO., Chicago, IL

A partnership of Walter B. Pearson and Charles Phelps, formed about 1892 to make screw machines/turret lathes in several sizes, including the No. 5 machine shown below. Pearson reorganized the firm as the PEARSON MACHINE CO. in 1900 and merged the firm into the Standard Screw Co. in 1902.

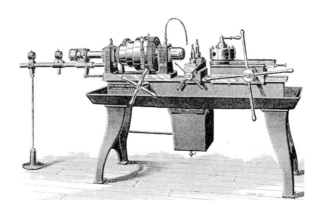

PEASE MACHINE TOOL CO., Worcester, MA

Formed in 1892 by George V. Rogers when he bought the assets of H.C. Pease & Co., a planer maker. Its sole product in 1892 appears to have been PRENTISS engine lathes, made for the Prentiss Tool & Supply Co., a large New York machinery dealer, as late as 1900. Prentiss sold the lathes under its own name as private label machines. The lathes were made in several sizes, including 17" (Fig.1) and 30" swing (Fig.2) models.

Fig.1   **Fig.2**

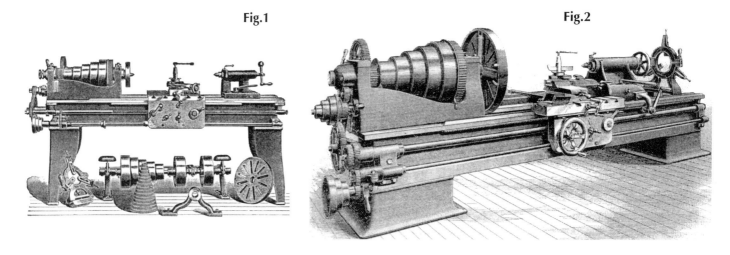

PERKINS, F.S., Lowell, MA, later
PERKINS CO., F.S., Lowell, MA

Founded by Francis S. Perkins (?-1900) in 1867 to make engine lathes, speed lathes and rack cutters. The firm employed 75 hands when Perkins died in 1900. The firm incorporated as F.S. PERKINS CO. in January, 1901, with a capital of $12,000; A.B. Woodworth was president and William E. Grady, secretary and manager.

Production in 1885 included engine lathes from 14" to 26" swing "in any bed length" (Fig.1). In 1896, engine lathes were offered in 16" (Fig.2), 18", 21", 24" (Fig.3), 30", and 36" (Fig.4) swings. Lathe production continued past 1904. *(continued on next page)*

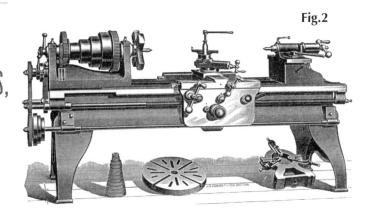

Fig.1

Fig.2

Fig.3

Fig.4

PHILADELPHIA ROLL & MACHINE WORKS, Philadelphia, PA

Formed in 1895 as a reorganization of the Bush Hill Iron Works. Maker of roll lathes for steel mills. In 1900, the firm made a variant roll lathe for turning granite columns at a quarry in Vinalhaven, ME (Fig.1). One of the largest lathes made, it would turn 78" in diameter and 60' in length and was equipped with four carriages with two cutting tools each.

The finished columns, used in construction of St. John the Divine Cathedral in New York City, were 6' in diameter, 54' long, and weighed 160 tons each. Note in the illustration below (Fig.2) that the lathe was installed in the open air, probably to ease handling of the columns. *(continued on next page)*

Fig.1

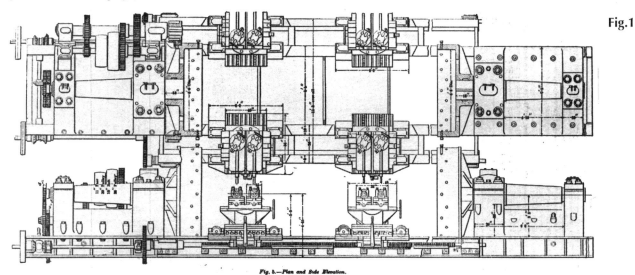

Fig. 5.—Plan and Side Elevation.

MAMMOTH GRANITE COLUMN CUTTING LATHE.

Fig.2

PHOENIX IRON WORKS, Hartford, CT

Operated by GEORGE S. LINCOLN & CO., a partnership of George S. Lincoln (1819-1894), and his brother Charles L. Lincoln (1825-1908), formed in 1846 to make a variety of large machine tools, but specializing in lathes, planers, and milling machines. The firm reorganized as LINCOLN & CO. when George S. Lincoln retired in 1885 and again as the PHOENIX IRON WORKS CO. when Lincoln's grandson, Charles L. Taylor took over in 1901.

Early production included engine lathes (Fig.1) offered in 20", 30" and 40" swings prior to 1854. In 1856, Phoenix offered an improved 16" engine lathe (Fig.2), designed by Amos Whitney who worked at Phoenix 1853-1860. Note the weighted rest, a feature notable on early PRATT & WHITNEY engine lathes. An engine lathe which could turn 10'6" and swing 7'2", with a bed of 18' (Fig.3) was also offered in 1856. Note the large span between the shears which allowed the large turning capacity.

Fig.1   Fig.2

Fig.3

PITTSBURG MACHINE TOOL CO., Pittsburgh, PA

Formed in 1899 to take over the lathe and planer lines previously made by the GLEASON WORKS. Frank Moore was president and F.J. Curtis secretary and general manager. Capital was $250,000.

Early products included Gleason design engine lathes from 26" to 60" swing. A new design, triple geared, 50" engine lathe (Fig.1) was introduced in 1902. An improved 28" model with quick change feed gear box (Fig.2) was introduced in 1907. Designed for heavy work, it weighed in at 8,000 lbs.

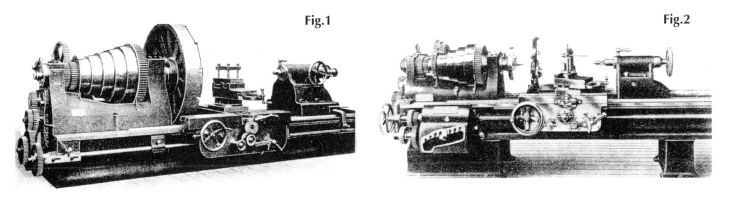

Fig.1   Fig.2

POND, D.W., Worcester, MA, later
POND MACHINE TOOL CO., Worcester, MA, later Plainfield, NJ

Founded by David W. Pond (1848-1897) in 1872 after leaving a partnership with his father Lucius W. Pond. Early production was almost entirely engine lathes and vertical drilling machines.

Pond bought out his father's creditors when L.W. POND failed in 1875, merged the firm with his own company and operated for a time as D.W. POND, SUCCESSOR TO L.W. POND. In 1882 Pond was the largest machine tool builder in Worcester, employing 240 men.

The firm was incorporated February 1, 1883, as the POND MACHINE TOOL CO. with D.W. Pond as president. The company moved to Plainfield, NJ, in 1887 with Pond now serving as superintendent. He sold his interest to MANNING, MAXWELL & MOORE in 1894 and shot himself August 4, 1897.

On August 15, 1899, the company merged with the NILES TOOL WORKS and BEMENT, MILES & CO. to form the NILES-BEMENT-POND CO. The POND MACHINE TOOL CO. continued to operate as a division.

Products in 1874 included engine lathes (Fig.1), 10" hand lathes (Fig.2) and 17" hand lathes (Fig.3). 1884 production included 19" and 20" engine lathes with compound rest (Fig.4) or plain rest (Fig.5), 22" and 24" engine lathes (Fig.6), 26", 30" and 32" engine lathes (Fig.7), 36", 40" and 42" engine lathes (Fig.8), and 60" engine lathes (Fig.9).

79" wheel lathes (Fig.10) and heavy engine lathes from 36" to 66" swing (Fig.11) were offered in 1890. Very heavy center drive lathes for turning steel wheels (Fig.12) were introduced in 1891. 1903 production included 42" facing lathes (Fig.13), 42" engine lathes with motor drive (Fig.14), and 32" projectile lathes for turning and boring 16" projectiles. *(continued on next 3 pages)*

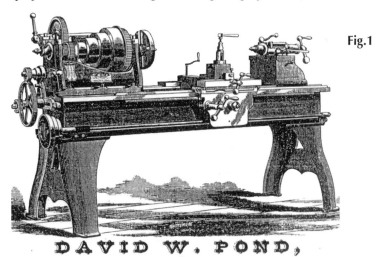

Fig.1

DAVID W. POND,

HAND LATHE WITH HOLLOW SPINDLE.   **Fig.2**

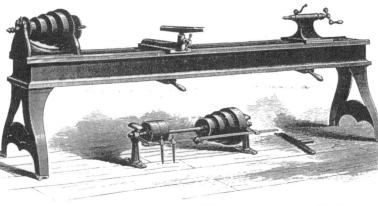

HAND LATHE.   **Fig.3**

WITH COMPOUND REST.   **Fig.4**

WITH PLAIN REST.   **Fig.5**

Fig.6

22 AND 24 INCH SWING.

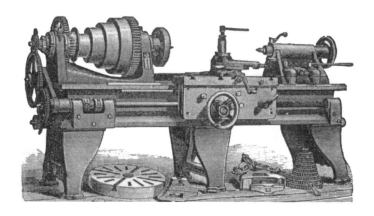

Fig.7

30, 32 AND 26 INCH SWING.

Fig.8

42, 40 AND 36 INCH SWING.

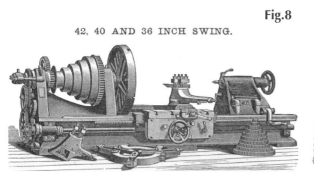

Fig.9

New Engine Lathe.—Sixty Inch Swing.

Fig.10

Fig.11

Fig.12

LATHE FOR TURNING STEEL-TIRED CAR WHEELS.

121

Fig.13

Fig.14

POND, L.W., Worcester, MA

Formed in 1856 by Lucius W. Pond (1826-1889) as a successor to SAMUEL FLAGG & CO., where Pond had been a partner. By 1858, Pond was offering "planers from 2 to 36 feet, engine lathes, and upright drills".

Pond took his son, David W. Pond, as a partner about 1869 but David Pond left to form his own company in 1872. L.W. Pond's business was taken over by his creditors in 1875 when he pled guilty to three counts of forgery and was sentenced to 15 years in prison. His son bought the firm from the creditors and merged it into D.W. POND.

Products included hand lathes offered in 1858 (Fig.1), and engine lathes in 1866 (Fig.2). Pond's 1874 catalog offered medium weight engine lathes (Fig.3) in 13", 15", 16" 18" swings; heavy weight engine lathes in 20" and 24" (Fig.4), 28" (Fig.5), 32" and 38" (Fig.6) swings; and triple geared models (Fig.7) in 40", 44", 54" 54" and 60" swings. *(continued on next page)*

Fig.1

LUCIUS W. POND,
(Successor to Samuel Flagg & Co.) Manufacturer of

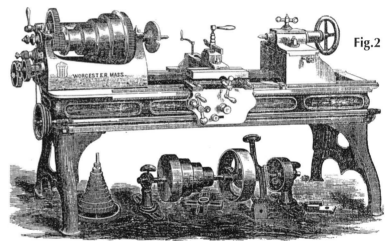

Fig.2

LUCIUS W. POND,

Fig.3

ENGINE LATHE, 18 INCHES SWING.

Fig.4

ENGINE LATHES, 20 AND 24 INCHES SWING.

POND, L.W.

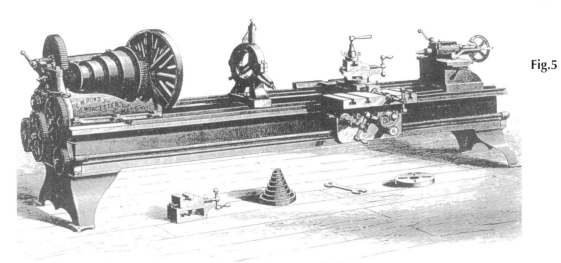

ENGINE LATHE, 28 INCHES SWING.

Fig.5

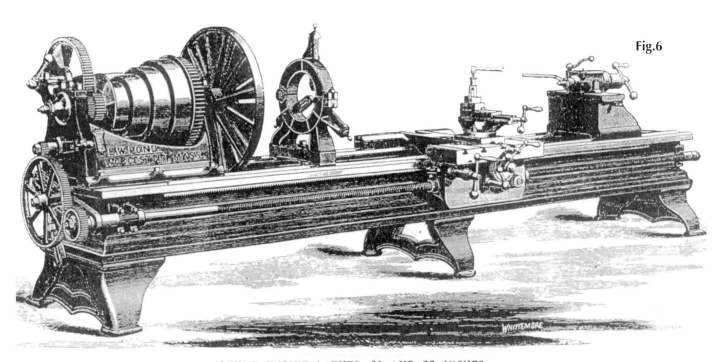

SWING ENGINE LATHES, 32 AND 38 INCHES.

Fig.6

ENGINE LATHES, 40, 44, 54 AND 60 INCHES SWING, WITH TRIPLE GEARS.

Fig.7

POOL & CO., A.A., Newark, NJ

Founded 1873 by Alex A. Pool to make engine lathes and combination lathes and milling machines. The firm ceased operation in 1883.

PORTER MACHINE WORKS, Hatfield, MA, later
PORTER & McLEOD TOOL CO., Hatfield, MA

Founded in 1884 by Johnathon E. Porter (1849-1921). Lathe production began in 1886 with the introduction of the Porter designed HATFIELD lathe. The firm reorganized as PORTER & McLEOD TOOL CO. when Porter's son-in-law, Hugh McLeod (1867-1927), joined him in 1898. McLeod became sole owner when Porter died in 1921.

Lathes offered in 1894 included 16" (Fig.1) engine lathes. 1898 production included 14" (Fig.2), 16" (Fig.3), 18", and 21" (Fig.4) engine lathes.

Fig.1

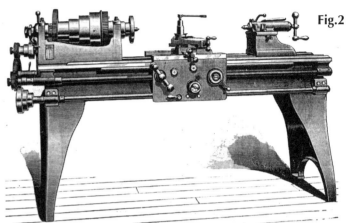
Fig.2

Fig.3

Fig.4

POTTER & JOHNSTON MACHINE CO., Pawtucket, RI

Formed in April, 1893, by James C. Potter (?-1925) and John Johnston to make manufacturing lathes and shapers. Johnston had previously been chief draftsman of the PRATT & WHITNEY CO. In 1911, the firm bought control of the WINDSOR MACHINE CO., a maker of turret lathes.

Early production included the No. 4 manufacturing lathe (Fig.1) and manufacturing turret lathes (Fig.2). Automatic manufacturing turret lathes (Fig.3) were introduced in 1903.

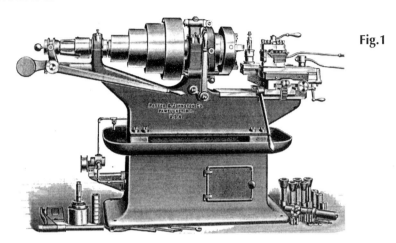

Fig.1

Fig.2

Fig.3

POWELL & CO., A.M., Worcester, MA, later
POWELL MACHINE TOOL CO., Worcester, MA

A partnership of Albert M. Powell (1857-1935) and George Carter, formed in 1881 as a reorganization of WIGHT & POWELL. In 1882 the firm employed 50 men making lathes and planers. *(continued on next page)*

Fig.1

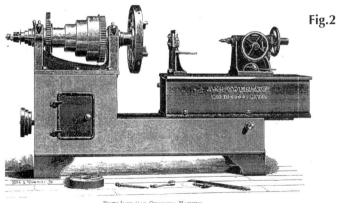

Fig.2

1881 production included engine lathes (Fig.1) and 50" gap chucking lathes (Fig.2). An improved 26" engine lathe (Fig.3) was introduced in 1882.

In 1884 the firm was purchased by George W. Fifield and others and reorganized as the POWELL MACHINE TOOL CO., which was absorbed by the L.W. POND MACHINE CO. in 1886.

Fig.3

PRATT, WHITNEY & CO., Hartford, CT, later
PRATT & WHITNEY CO., Hartford, CT

A partnership of Francis A. Pratt (1827-1902) and Amos Whitney (1832-1920), formed in 1860 to make silk machinery, lathes, and planers. Both had previously worked at the PHOENIX IRON WORKS where Pratt was superintendent and Whitney a contractor.

The firm incorporated as the PRATT & WIIITNEY CO. in 1869. Employment in 1883 was 675 hands, increasing to 1,160 in 1896. Pratt served as president until his retirement in 1898; Whitney was superintendent, becoming president in 1898. In January, 1901, Whitney sold out to the NILES-BEMENT-POND CO., which continued operation of the PRATT & WHITNEY CO. as a division.

Lathe production in the mid-1860s included speed lathes in 12" and 15" swings, engine lathes from 15" to 8' swings, and engine lathes equipped with Slate's patent taper attachment (Fig.1). *(continued on next 5 pages)*

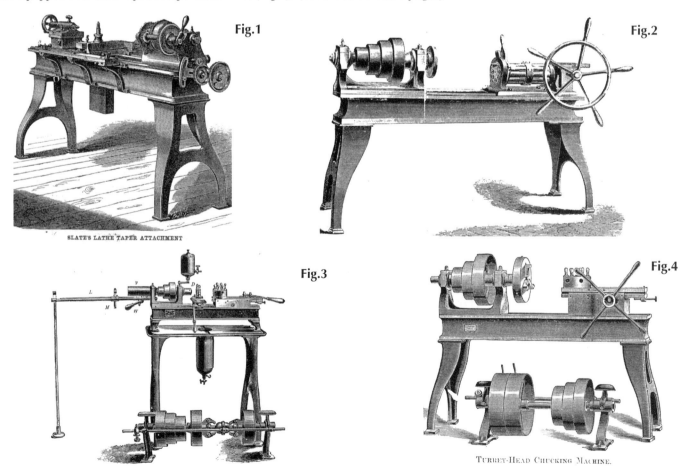

SLATE'S LATHE TAPER ATTACHMENT

Fig.1

Fig.2

Fig.3

Fig.4

TURRET-HEAD CHUCKING MACHINE.

Edward G. Parkhurst (1830-1901), who had joined Pratt & Whitney in 1869 as assistant superintendent, invented the wire or rod feed for lathe spindles in 1871, making possible the automatic screw machine.

Chucking lathes with horizontal axis turrets (Fig.2) were offered by 1876. 1881 production included small screw machines with the Parkhurst wire feed (Fig.3), 18" turret head chucking lathes (Fig.4), 52" gap bed chucking lathes (Fig.5), and turret head engine lathes in 28" (Fig.6) and 36" swings.

Products offered in 1884 included 19" engine lathes (Fig.7), 50" pulley lathes (Fig.8), a new 27" lathe (Fig.9), and No. 3 (Fig.10) and No. 4 (Fig.11) screw machines. 18" turret chucking lathes (Fig.12) were introduced in 1886. Turret head engine lathes (Fig.13) with 21" swing and 2 1/8" spindle hole, and chucking lathes (Fig.14) with 21" to 36" swings were introduced in 1889. Production in 1893 included 16" brass finishing lathes(Fig.15), 16" turret chucking lathes (Fig.16), 19" facing and chucking lathes (Fig.17), 30" turret chucking lathes (Fig.18), and improved No. 4 screw machines (Fig.19).

Other 1890s lathe offerings included 10" tool makers' lathes (Fig.20) introduced in 1893, and turret head threading lathes (Fig.21) introduced in 1895. 16" weighted engine lathes (Fig.22), 21" gibbed engine lathes (Fig.23), 10" or 12" turret lathes (Fig.24) and 14" (Fig.25) turret lathes were introduced in 1897.

Improved 14" engine lathes (Fig.26) were introduced in 1900 and newly designed turret lathes with capacity for 7½" work through the spindle in 1901.

1903 production included 7" bench lathes (Fig.27), improved 10" toolmakers' lathes (Fig.28), 14" engine lathes (Fig.29), NEW MODEL 5/8"x 4½" turret lathes (Fig.30), 1" x 10" turret lathes (Fig.31), and 2" x 26" turret lathes (Fig.32).

New products in 1907 included 16" toolroom lathes with quick change feed (Fig.33) and a choice of cone pulley or all geared head, and a geared head 2½" x 26" turret lathe.

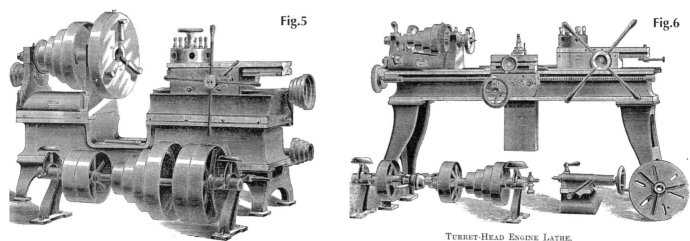

Fig.5

52-Inch Chucking Machine.

Fig.6

Turret-Head Engine Lathe.

Fig.7

Fig.8

Fig.9

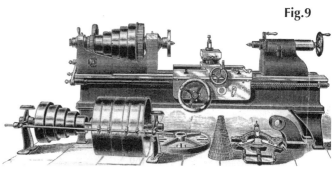

Fig.10

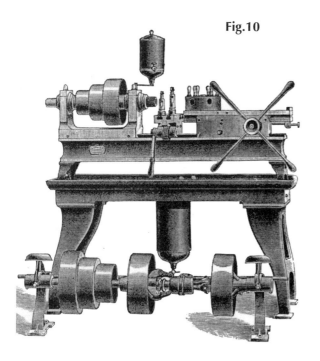

Fig.11

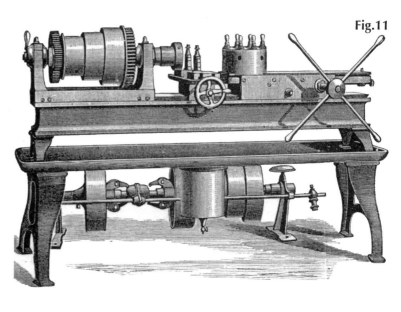

Fig.12

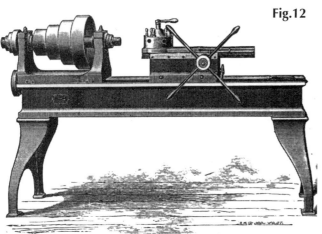

Fig.13

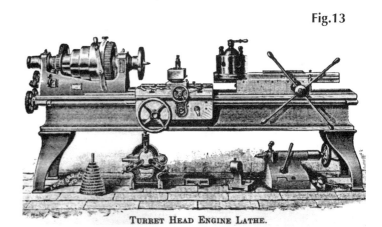

TURRET HEAD ENGINE LATHE.

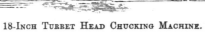

18-INCH TURRET HEAD CHUCKING MACHINE.

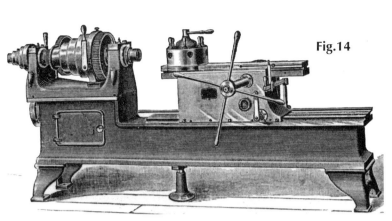

Fig.14

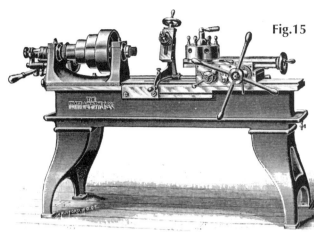

Fig.15

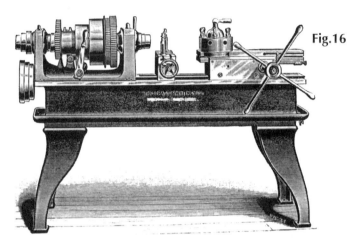

Fig.16

Fig.17

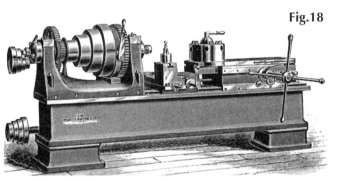

Fig.18

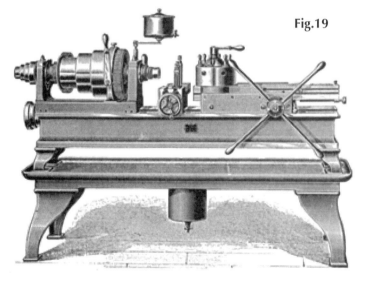

Fig.19

Fig.20

10-INCH TOOL MAKERS' ENGINE LATHE.

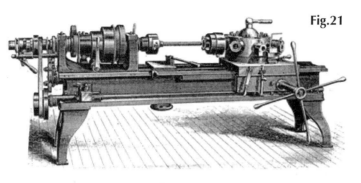

Fig.21

PRATT & WHITNEY TURRET HEAD THREADING LATHE.

Fig.22

Fig.23

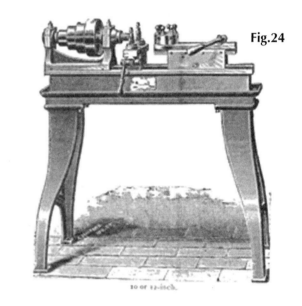

Fig.24

10 or 12-inch.

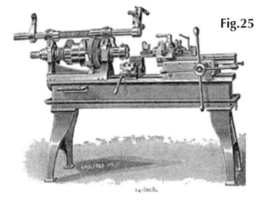

Fig.25

14-inch.

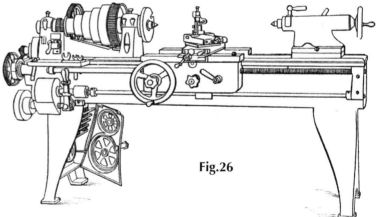

Fig.26

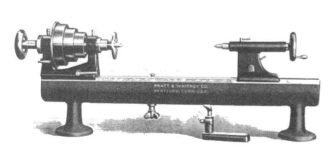

Fig.27

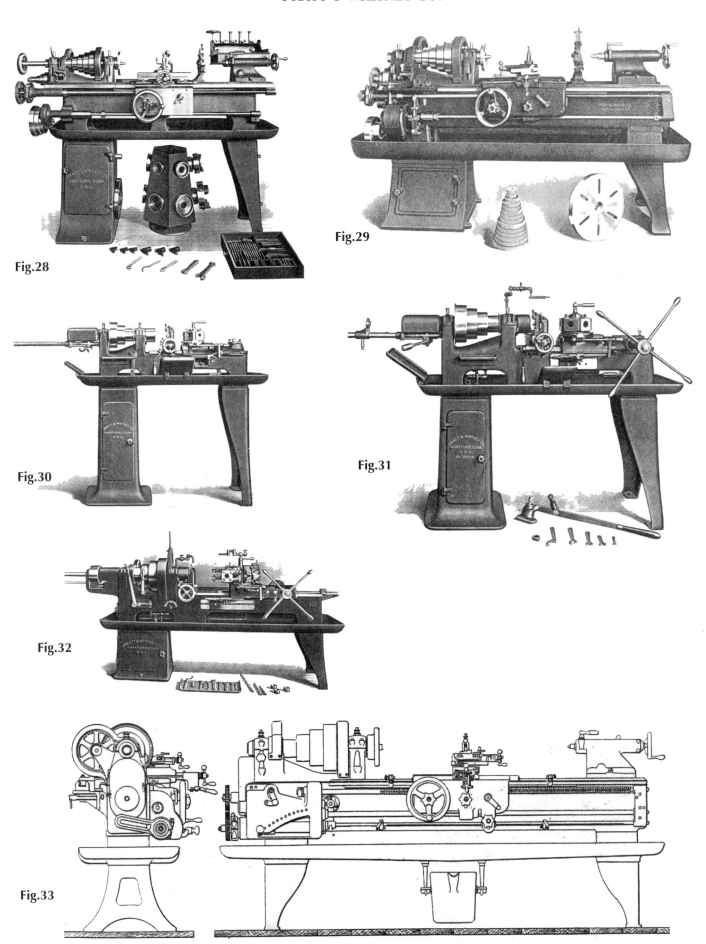

Fig.28

Fig.29

Fig.30

Fig.31

Fig.32

Fig.33

PRENTICE & CO., A.F., Worcester, MA

A partnership of Albert F. Prentice (1841-1902) and his brother Vernon F. Prentice (1839-1926), formed in 1872. Products included 11" foot-power lathes (Fig.1), 9" hand lathes, larger hand lathes in 11", 14" and 16" swings (Fig.2), and bench lathes (Fig.3) in 9" and 11" sizes.

In 1877 Prentice sold out to Frederick E. Reed who continued lathe production, including 11" new engine lathes (Fig.4), as A.F. PRENTICE & CO. until reorganizing as F.E. REED in 1881.

FOOT LATHES.

HAND LATHES.

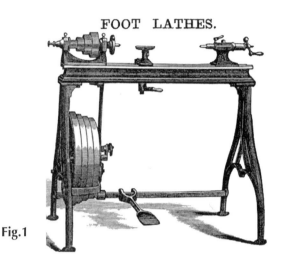

Fig.1

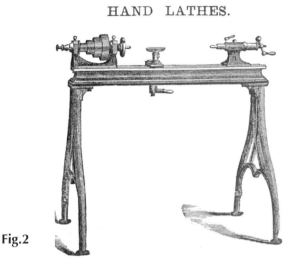

Fig.2

Fig.3

BENCH LATHES.

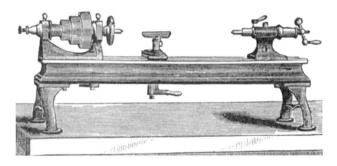

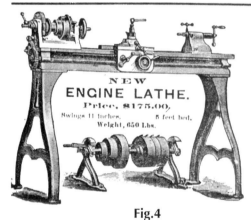

Fig.4

PRENTICE & CO. B.W., Worcester, MA, later
PRENTICE BROTHERS CO., Worcester, MA

A partnership of Benjamin W. Prentice and his brother Vernon F. Prentice (1839-1926), formed in 1877. Early production consisted of 11" foot-power (Fig.1) and countershaft driven (Fig.2) lathes in the same pattern as those made by A.F. PRENTICE & CO. By 1880, Prentice was offering engine lathes in 11", 14" and 16" swings, hand lathes from 10" to 20" swings, and foot power lathes.

In 1881, a third brother, Albert F. Prentice (1841-1902) joined the firm which then reorganized as PRENTICE BROTHERS CO. 1881 production was 36 to 40 upright drills and 12 lathes per month. The firm operated until April 1, 1912, when it consolidated with F.E. REED to form the REED-PRENTICE CO.

PRENTICE BROTHERS CO. continued production of earlier designs, including 10" and 11" foot lathes (Fig.3), and by 1884 began making 15" engine lathes (Fig.4). A new line of engine lathes in 12" (Fig.5) to 24" swing (Fig.6) was introduced in 1891, with a 24" double-geared model (Fig.7), offered in 1892. A new design 11" lathe, equipped with a double back geared head, was introduced in 1894 in foot power (Fig.8) and countershaft (Fig.9) versions.

In 1895 a new 12" engine lathe (Fig.10) was introduced. Specially designed for taper work, the entire head and tail stock assemblies were made to pivot as a unit. Improved engine lathes (Fig.11) in 12" to 24" swing, with optional taper attachments (Fig.12), and stud lathes (Fig.13) in 12" and 16" swings, were offered by 1895 as were the company's first electrically driven lathes (Fig.14).

By 1903, Albert E. Newton (1876-1941) was head of machine design and was appointed superintendent and general manager in 1909. Newton designs included engine lathes with quick change feed gear boxes introduced in 1904 in 16" cone head (Fig.15) and geared head versions, and 18" engine lathes for use with high speed steel tooling in belt and electric motor (Fig.16) versions, introduced in 1905. Geared head 15" turret lathes (Fig.17) with quick change feed gear boxes were introduced in 1906. *(continued on next 2 pages)*

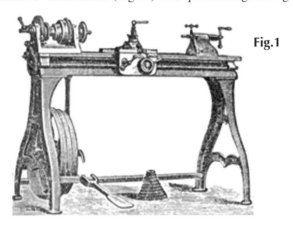

Fig.1 **Fig.2**

10 AND 11 INCH ENGINE LATHES.   15 INCH SWING ENGINE LATHE.

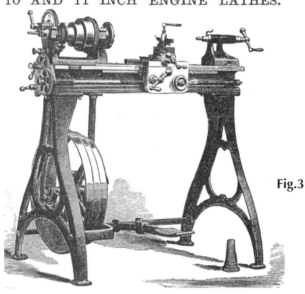

Fig.3

Fig.4

Fig.5

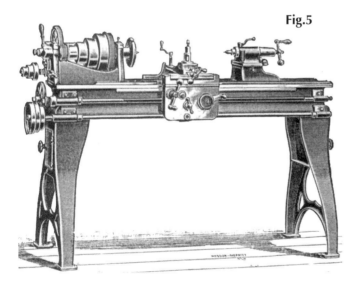

Fig.6

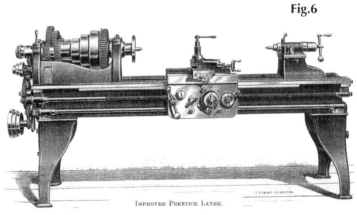

IMPROVED PRENTICE LATHE.

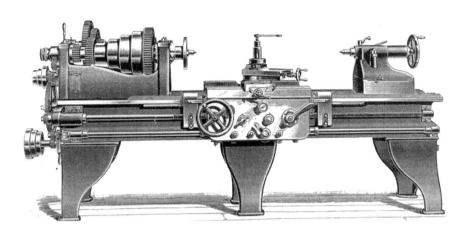

Fig.7

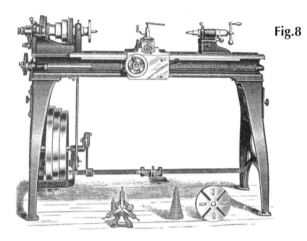

Fig.8

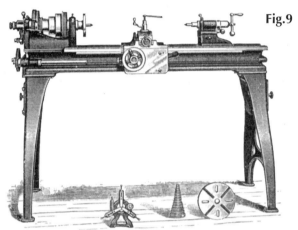

Fig.9

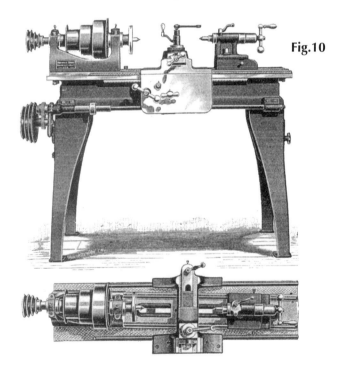

Fig.10

Fig.11

Taper Attachment

FOR

14, 16, 18, 21 and 24-inch Engine Lathes.

Fig.12

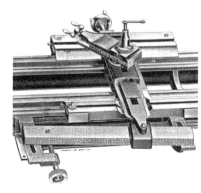

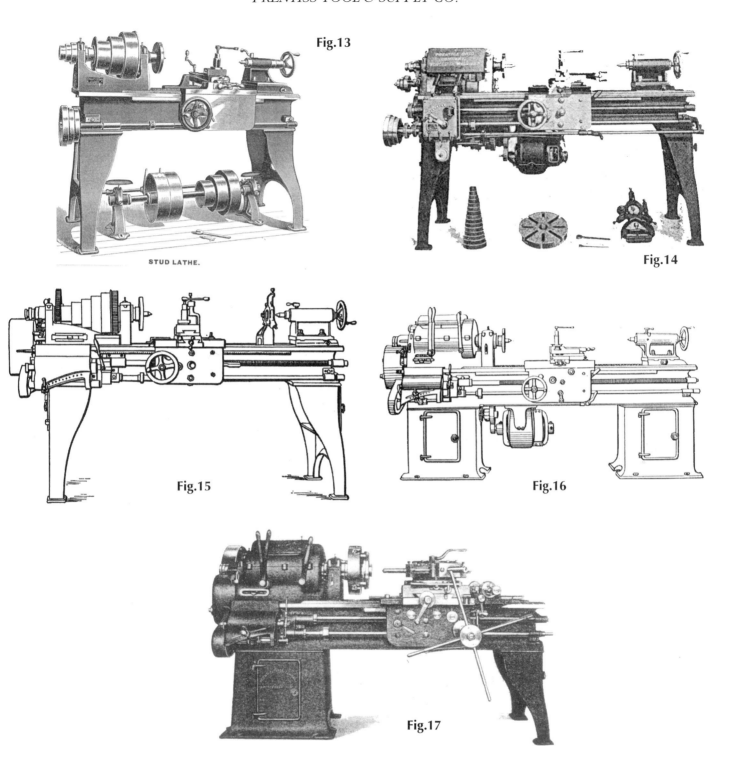

Fig.13

STUD LATHE.

Fig.14

Fig.15

Fig.16

Fig.17

PRENTISS TOOL & SUPPLY CO., New York, NY

A large machinery dealer, the firm sold private label lathes made for them by H.C. FISH MACHINE WORKS and PEASE MACHINE TOOL CO. in the 1890's. It also offered the HODGE-FRAZIER taper turning attachment *(next page)* in 1893. Designed to be used on any lathe of adequate size and easily changed from one lathe to another, it was offered under the Prentiss name but was probably made by another firm.

THE HODGE-FRAZIER TAPER TURNING ATTACHMENT.

PROGRESS MACHINE WORKS, Baltimore, MD
See JACKSON & TYLER

PUTNAM, J. & S.W., Fitchburg, MA, later
PUTNAM & CO., J. & S.W., Fitchburg, MA, later
PUTNAM MACHINE CO., Fitchburg, MA

A partnership of John Putnam (1810-1888) and his brother Salmon W. Putnam (1815-1872) formed in 1836 in Ashburnham, MA, moving to Fitchburg, MA, in 1838. Lathes were offered as early as 1838 (Fig.1).

The brothers reorganized as J. & S.W. PUTNAM & CO. in 1850 when Charles H. Brown and Benjamin Snow were admitted as partners and again as the PUTNAM MACHINE CO. when John Q. Wright, Sylvester Wright and Charles Burleigh were admitted in August, 1854.

Salmon W. Putnam served as president from 1858, when the firm became a stock company, until his death in 1872. John Putnam was not active in company management after 1858. Salmon W. Putnam, Jr. (1844-1923) managed the firm from 1872 until 1882 when, with his brother George E. Putnam (1854-1892), he left to form a competing firm, the PUTNAM TOOL CO. (S.W. PUTNAM'S SONS).

The PUTNAM TOOL CO. was merged into the PUTNAM MACHINE CO. March 18, 1886, a few months after Salmon W. Putnam, Jr. and his brother rejoined and gained control of the PUTNAM MACHINE CO. Salmon W. Putnam, Jr. served as vice president until selling the firm to MANNING, MAXWELL & MOORE in 1913. George E. Putnam served as superintendent until his death in 1892.

The firm made a wide variety of machine tools including planers, shapers, and slotters. Lathes included 16" engine lathes (Fig.2) offered in 1860. The 1877 catalog offered 8½" hand lathes, 13" hand lathes (Fig.3), 14" engine lathes (Fig.4), 18" engine lathes (Fig.5), 44" extra heavy engine lathes (Fig.6), and car axle lathes (Fig.7).

Pulley lathes with 40", 50" (Fig.8) and 64" swings were offered by 1884. 1887 production included engine lathes in both the PUTNAM TOOL CO. pattern (Fig.9) and the PUTNAM MACHINE CO. pattern (Fig.10).

New Model 14" engine lathes (Fig.11) and 120", 98" and 86" pit lathes (Fig.12) were offered in 1892. An 1899 catalog offered 12" and 14" engine lathes (Fig.13), 15" engine lathes, 16" engine lathes (Fig.14), 18" engine lathes, and double axle lathes (Fig.15). The entire line of ex-PUTNAM TOOL CO. engine lathes in swings from 20" to 76" was also offered.

1901 production included 14" engine lathes (Fig.16), 16" engine lathes, 22" engine lathes (Fig.17), 24", 26" and 28" engine lathes, 30" and 36" engine lathes (Fig.18). Triple geared models were offered in 38", 42" and 48" engine lathes (Fig.19), 54" and 62" engine and pit lathes (Fig.20), and 76" engine lathes (Fig.21). Other lathes included 79", 84" and 90" driving wheel lathes (Fig.22), 16/32" and 19/43" extension gap lathes (Fig.23), and 21/37" and 25/50" gap chucking lathes (Fig.24).

In 1904, a 32", electric motor driven lathe (Fig.25) was exhibited at the World's Fair to demonstrate high cutting rates possible with high speed steel tools. The company claimed metal removal rates up to three tons per hour. *(continued on next 5 pages)*

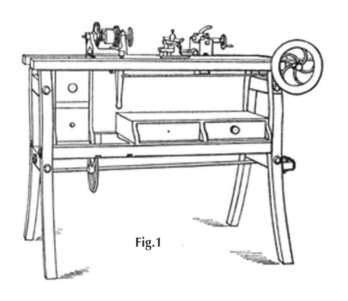

Fig.1

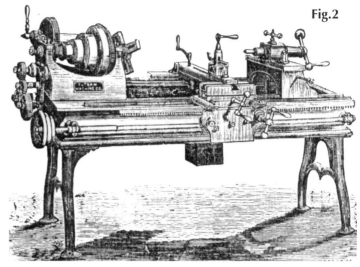

Fig.2

Fig.3

13 Inch Swing Hand Lathe.

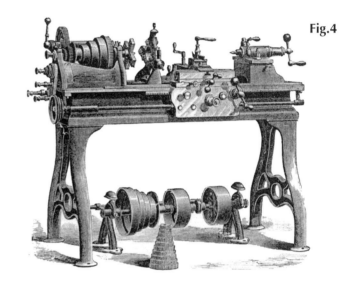

Fig.4

Fig.5

Fig.6

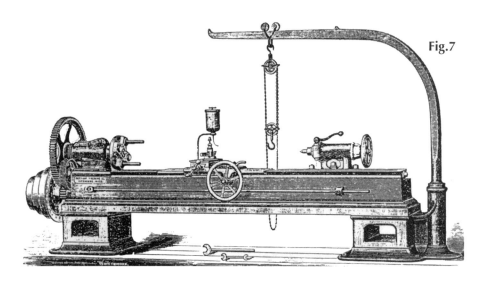

Fig.7

Fig.8

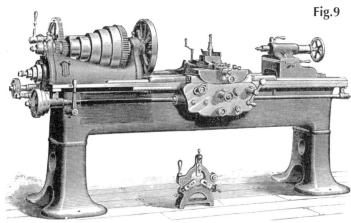

Fig.9

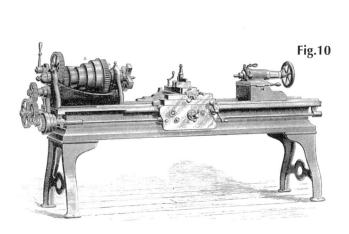

Fig.10

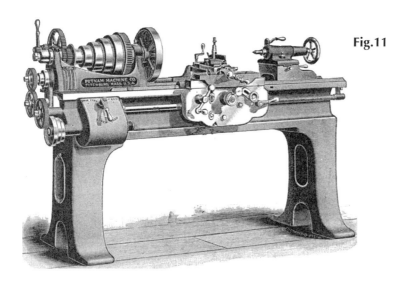

Fig.11

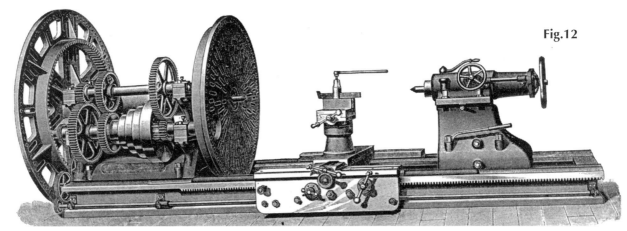

Fig.12

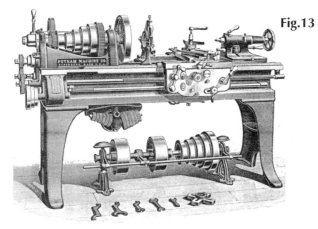

Fig.13

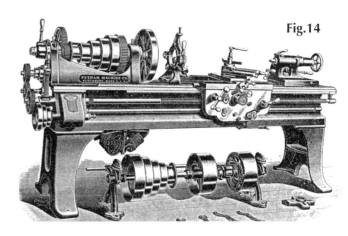

Fig.14

Fig.15

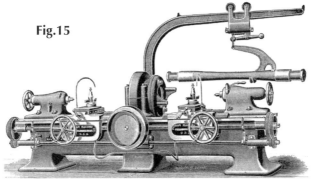

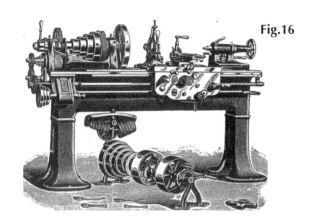

Fig.16

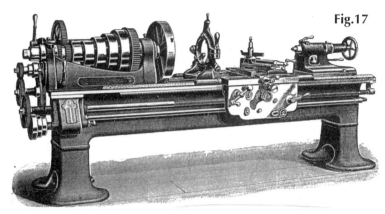

Fig.17

Fig.18

Fig.19

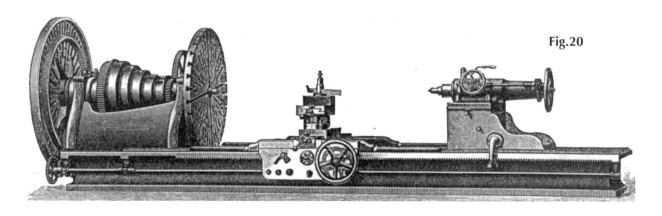

Fig.20

Fig.21

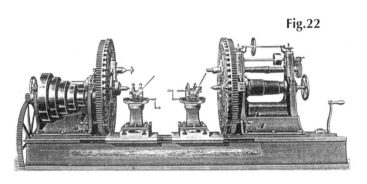

Fig.22

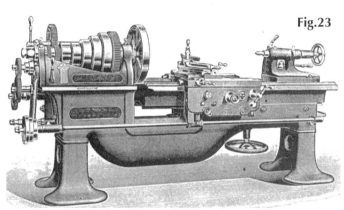

Fig.23

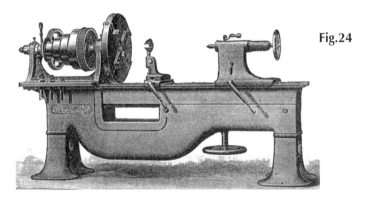

Fig.24

Fig.25

PUTNAM TOOL CO. (S.W. PUTNAM'S SONS), Fitchburg, MA

Formed in 1882 by Salmon W. Putnam, Jr. and his brother George E. Putnam when they left the PUTNAM MACHINE CO., founded by their father and operated by members of the Putnam family. The firm was short-lived and was merged into the PUTNAM MACHINE CO. March 18, 1886, shortly after the brothers had rejoined and taken control of the family firm.

Products included new pattern makers' lathes (Fig.1); 16" engine lathes (Fig.2); New Pattern 46" (Fig.3), 62", and 76" engine lathes (Fig.4); and New Standard engine gap lathes with 28/57" (Fig.5) and 16/32" swings.

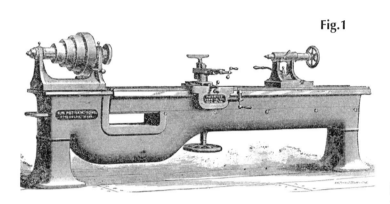

Fig.1

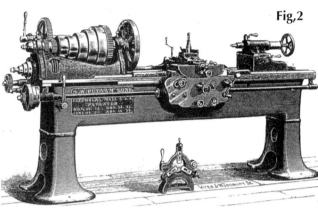

Fig,2

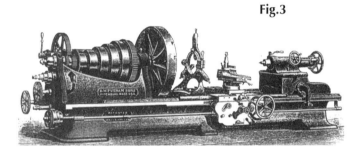

Fig.3

Fig.4

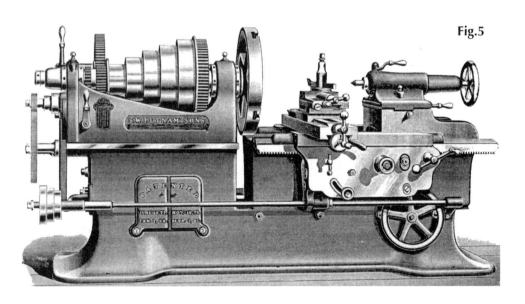

Fig.5

QUASSAICK MACHINE SHOP, Newburgh, NY

Maker, c1866-1867, of a variety of steam engines and machinery, including the Leonard & Clark engine lathe. The 1867 advertisement at right offered the Leonard & Clark engine lathe in 16" swing at $650 and 18" swing at $850.

QUASSAICK MACHINE SHOP,
Newburgh, N.Y.,
Manufactures
Iron and Wood-working Machinery,
Portable and Stationary Steam Engines, etc., etc.
Leonard & Clark Premium Lathes.
On hand—Two 16-inch, 8 ft. 6 inch. bed, price $650 each.
Five 18-inch, 15 ft. bed, price $850 each.
Wood's improved Molding and Planing Machines—will plane, tongue and groove 30 to 40 feet per minute—price $650.
New and staple machinery manufactured to order or by contract as required. 5 1

QUEEN CITY MACHINE WORKS, Cincinnati, OH

Operated by the partnership of Peter W. Reinshagen and John H. Buckman from 1868 to 1883. The firm made a variety of machine tools, including lathes patented July 18, 1882, by Reinhshagen.

RAHN & MAYER, Cincinnati, OH, later
RAHN & MAYER CO., Cincinnati, OH, later
RAHN, MAYER & CARPENTER CO., Cincinnati, OH, later
RAHN-CARPENTER CO., Cincinnati, OH

Formed in 1897 by John Rahn (1862-1921) and Charles F. Mayer to make 16" and 18" engine lathes. The partners reorganized in March, 1899, as the RAHN & MAYER CO. and again as the RAHN, MAYER & CARPENTER CO. when W.H. Carpenter was admitted in September, 1899. Mayer left in 1910 and the remaining partners reorganized as the RAHN-CARPENTER CO., which, on January 1, 1911, became the RAHN-LARMON CO.

Products offered in 1899 included 20/26" gap engine lathes (Fig.1). A line of engine lathes with 16" to 32" swings (Fig.2) was offered by 1903. Improved gap lathes (Fig.3) with swings of 16/23", 19/25" and 20/26" were introduced in 1907.

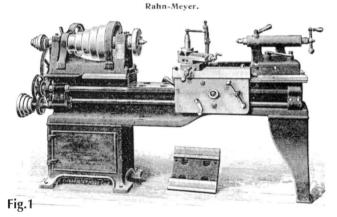

Fig.1

Fig.2

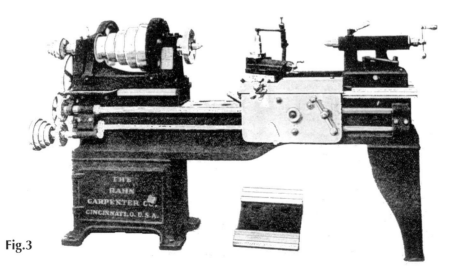

Fig.3

REED, F.E., Worcester, MA, later
REED & CO., F.E., Worcester, MA, later
REED CO., F.E., Worcester, MA

Formed in 1881 by Frederick E. Reed (1847-1917) as a reorganization of A.F. PRENTICE & CO. Reed had been a partner in A.F. PRENTICE & CO. before buying the firm in 1877. With an employment of 50 hands, Reed continued production of Prentice 12" foot-power lathes (Fig.1), 12" engine lathes (Fig.2) and hand lathes (Fig.3). He also began making larger lathes, including a 15" model (Fig.4) introduced in 1881.

The firm became F.E. REED & CO. when John R. Back was admitted as a partner January 1, 1891. It incorporated as the F.E. REED CO. in 1894 with 150 hands. Production continued to increase and, in 1909, it was able to claim that 24,000 lathes had been produced since 1881. Reed retired in 1912 when the firm was merged with PRENTICE BROTHERS CO. to form the REED-PRENTICE CO.

1884 production included new pattern 10" and 11" foot-power lathes (Fig.5), 10" engine lathes (Fig.6), and 11" engine lathes (Fig.7). Medium sized 14" (Fig.8) and 16" engine lathes (Fig.9) were offered with a choice of plain or rise and fall tool rests. Heavier engine lathes in 18" (Fig.10), 22", and 26" (Fig.11) swings were also available. An improved 12" foot-power lathe (Fig.12) was introduced in 1896.

Production in 1899 included 10" foot-power lathes (Fig.13), and 10" engine lathes (Fig.14) with elevating rests and friction feed; and hand lathes in 12" (Fig.15) 14", 16" and 26" swings. Engine lathes included 12" swing with elevating rest and power cross feed (Fig.16), 14" swing in plain and power cross feed (Fig.17) models, and 16"swing with power cross feed (Fig.18). Heavy engine lathes included 18" swing (Fig.19), 20" swing, 24" swing (Fig.20), 27" swing, and 30" swing.

12" taper-turning engine lathes (Fig.21) were offered in 1901. The 24" SPECIAL lathe, with two patented elevating tool posts (Fig.22) was introduced in 1902. Electric motor drives (Fig.23) were available by 1904 and a geared feed model (Fig.24), with quick change gear box for eight feeds, was introduced in 1907. *(continued on next 4 pages)*

12 INCH.   **Fig.1**

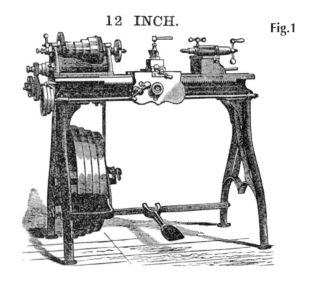

12 INCH SWING.   **Fig.2**

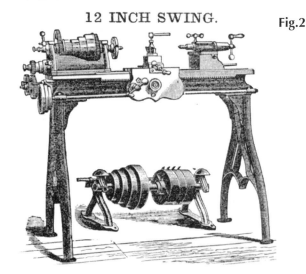

Fig3

Fig.4

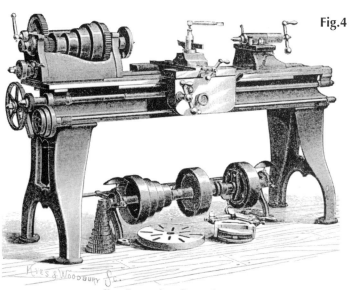

NEW FIFTEEN-INCH ENGINE LATHE.

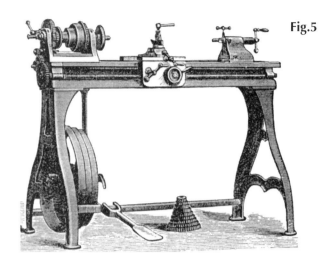

Fig.5

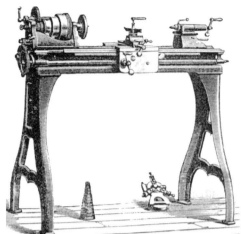
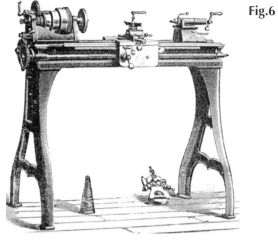

Fig.6

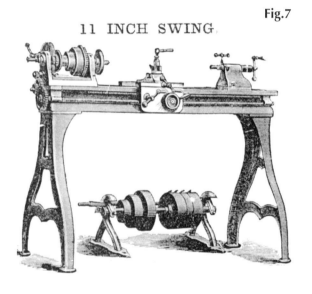

Fig.7

11 INCH SWING.

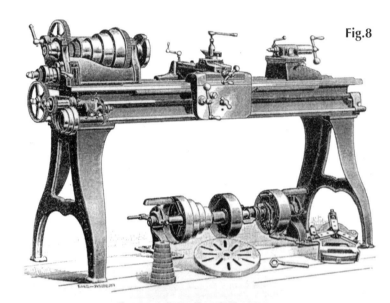

Fig.8

FOURTEEN-INCH ENGINE LATHE.

16 INCH SWING, EITHER PLAIN OR RAISE AND FALL GIB REST.

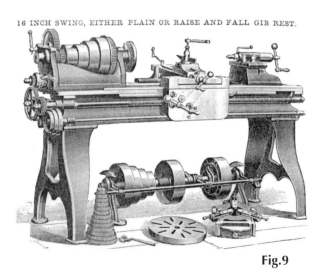

Fig.9

Fig.10

Fig.11

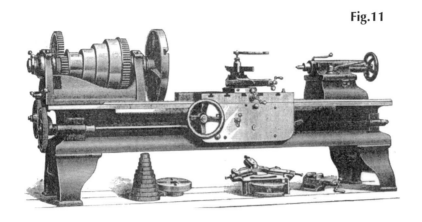

Fig.12

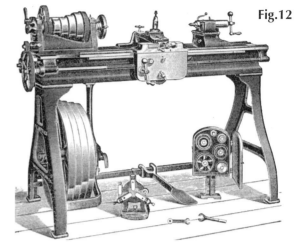

Fig.13

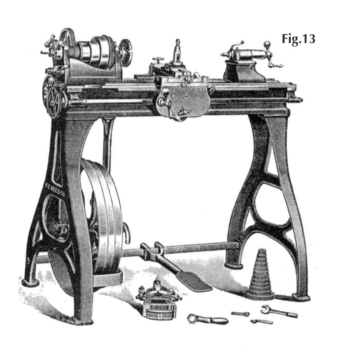

Fig.14

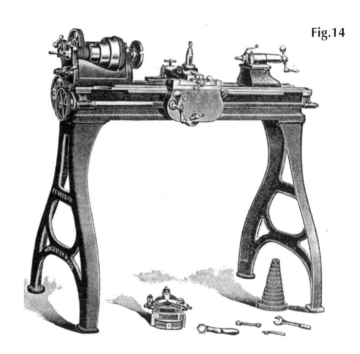

Fig.15

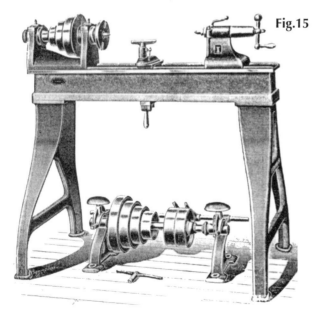

Fig.16

COMPOUND REST AND POWER CROSS FEED. **Fig.17**

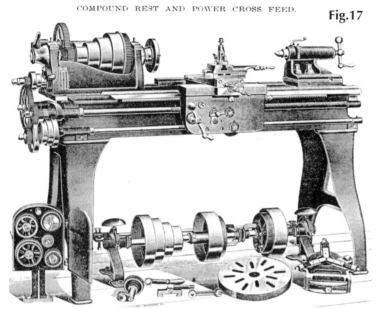

Fig.18

Fig.19

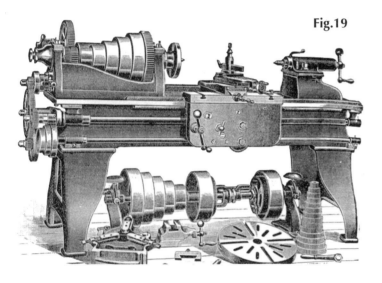

Fig.20

Fig.21

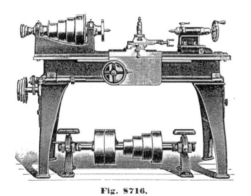

Fig. 8716.

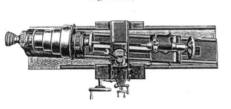

Fig.22

WITH TWO PATENTED ELEVATING TOOL POSTS.

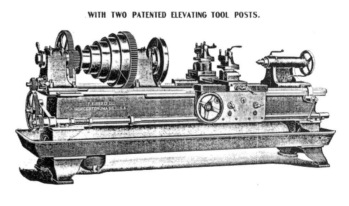

Fig.23   Fig.24

RESEK MACHINE TOOL CO., Cleveland, OH

Founded in 1903, the firm probably failed by 1905. Maker of the Resek DUPLEX lathe that mounted two short 12" engine lathes on a single bed.

REXFORD, RICHARD W., Philadelphia, PA

Maker, in 1883, of bench drills and light duty, 7" engine lathes such as that shown at right.

RHEYDT, FERDINAND, Chicago, IL

Maker, in 1870, of an engine lathe adapted for turning bolts and nuts from square or hex stock fed through the spindle. Bolt blanks were made using hollow mills mounted on the carriage; nut blanks were drilled using a separate feed motion in the carriage, patented December 29, 1868.

The machine could be used as an engine lathe by mounting the tail stock shown under the lathe in the illustration at left.

RICHARDSON, SAMUEL, Rochester, NY

Maker, in 1849, of engine and hand lathes, and "iron work of all descriptions."

RICHMOND CITY MILL WORKS, Richmond, IN

Founded in 1876 to make flour mill machinery. In 1887 the proprietor, Peter Shellenback, began making pulley lathes (below) for which he was granted a patent June 14, 1887.

In 1890, the lathe business was sold to Micajah C. Henley who then formed a new firm, the HENLEY MACHINE TOOL WORKS. Shellenback also started a new firm, the SHELLENBACK MACHINE TOOL CO.

PULLEY LATHE.

RIDER, JOHN F.C., South Newmarket, NH

Maker of engine lathes and steam engines, operating c1867-1882. Rider was granted a patent for an engine lathe on April 18, 1871.

RIDGEWAY MACHINE TOOL WORKS
Ridgeway, PA

Formed in 1904 by Harry R. Hyde to make large machine tools including engine lathes and driving wheel lathes. The company was acquired by the NILES-BEMENT-POND CO. in 1906.

1905 production included the 90", motor-driven driving wheel lathe shown at left.

RIVETT LATHE MFG. CO., Boston, MA

Formed about 1900 as a reorganization of the FANEUIL WATCH TOOL CO. operated by Edward Rivett (1851-1937). Rivett sold out in 1912 and the firm reorganized as the RIVETT LATHE & GRINDER MFG. CO.

Products offered in their 1903 catalog included No.3½ bench lathes (Fig.1); No. 4 bench lathes (Fig.2) available with milling attachment (Fig.3), screw cutting attachment (Fig.4), relieving attachment (Fig.5), and turret attachment (Fig.6); No.5 manufacturers' lathes (Fig.7), also available in a screw machine version (Fig.8); 8" lathes (Fig.9) available with milling attachment (Fig.10), spiral attachment (Fig.11), slotting attachment (Fig.12), and taper attachment (Fig.13). *(continued on next two pages)*

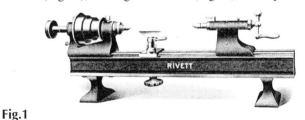

Fig.1

Rivett No. 3½ Bench Lathe
Weight, 90 lbs.

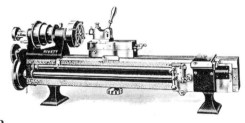

Fig.2

Rivett Precision Lathe
With Slotting Attachment Mounted on Base of Forming Slide

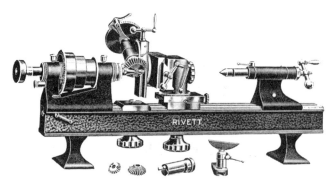

Rivett No. 4 Bench Lathe

With Slide Rest and Milling Attachment

Fig.3

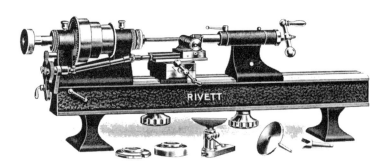

Rivett No. 4 Bench Lathe

With Screw Cutting Attachment for Slide Rest

Fig.4

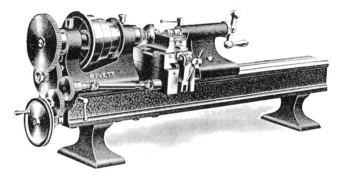

Rivett No. 4 Bench Lathe

With Relieving Attachment

Fig.5

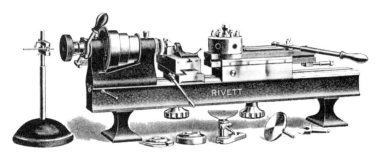

Rivett No. 4 Bench Lathe fitted up as a Screw Machine

With Turret Attachment and Cutting-off and Forming Slide, and Automatic Chuck Closer

Fig.6

Rivett Manufacturers' Lathe No. 5

Weight : Lathe, 165 lbs. ; Slide Rest, 17 lbs.

Fig.7

Rivett Manufacturers' Lathe No. 5

Fig.8

Rivett 8-Inch Precision Lathe

Weight, 250 lbs.

Fig.9

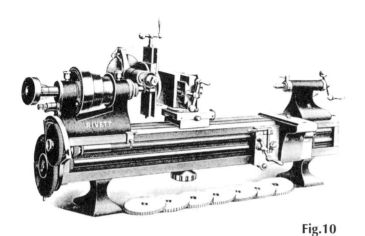

Fig.10

8-Inch Precision Lathe
With Slide Rest and Milling Attachment

Fig.11

8-Inch Precision Lathe
With Spiral Attachment and Traverse Miller

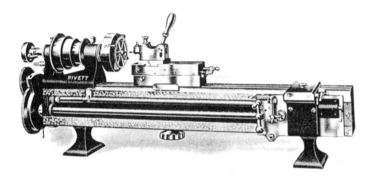

Fig.12

Rivett Precision Lathe
With Slotting Attachment Mounted on Base of Forming Slide

Fig.13

Rivett Precision Lathe, with Taper Attachment

ROBBINS, ERNEST F., Burrville, CT

Maker, in 1894, of an index milling attachment "intended to do all the milling required of screw machines and monitor or FOX lathes." It was supplied with a 48 position index plate or with a gear as shown at right.

INDEX MILLING ATTACHMENT FOR LATHES.

ROBBINS & LAWRENCE CO., Windsor, VT

Formed in 1850 by Samuel E. Robbins (1810-1874) and Richard S. Lawrence (1817-1892) as a reorganization of Robbins, Kendall & Lawrence. Primary products were a variety of firearms, most made on contract for the U.S. and British governments. Machine tools soon became a secondary product when they began selling machines that had been designed for their own firearms production.

Robbins, who was a Bangor, ME, businessman, served as president and Lawrence as superintendent, until the firm failed in 1856. The plant and equipment were bought in 1859 by Ebenezer G. Lamson, who then organized LAMSON, GOODNOW & YALE. Lawrence moved to Hartford, CT, where he became superintendent of the Sharps Rifle Mfg. Co.

Machine tool production included chain feed engine lathes, patented June 21, 1853, by Frederick W. Howe (1822-1891), and small turret lathes/screw machines also designed by Howe. The latter were called "Screw Milling Machines" by Robbins & Lawrence and only later variously called turret lathes, screw machines, and after the Civil War, monitor lathes. *(illustration next page)*

151

Screw machines offered by both PRATT & WHITNEY and J.R. BROWN & SHARPE by 1861 were direct descendants of the Howe design.

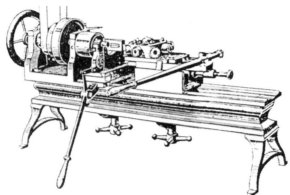

ROBBINS, L., Worcester, MA, later
ROBBINS MACHINE CO., Worcester, MA

    Founded by Lafayette Robbins about 1893 to make lathes and other machine tools. In 1908, he incorporated as the ROBBINS MACHINE CO., which operated into the 1920s.
    Lathe production included 13" and 15" engine lathes such as shown in the 1908 advertisement below.

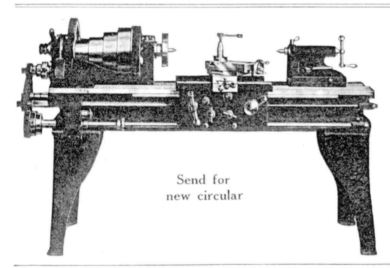

Send for
new circular

Robbins New Model
Standard Engine Lathes

    This cut represents our 13" and 15" lathes with compound rest.
    These lathes are common-sense tools, and have all the advantages for economic production, without expensive complicated attachments.
    The head and tail spindles are cast crucible steel. The head is powerfully back-geared, with extra wide cone belts, and speeds are arranged in regular gradation. The lathe is equipped with both belt and geared feeds. The rest has extra long bearings on the ways and is securely gibbed. The workmanship is of the best.

The Robbins Machine Company
149 Lagrange St., Worcester, Mass.

ROLLINS & CO., GEORGE A., Nashua, NH

    Maker, c1850-1865, of machine tools including engine lathes equipped with Rollin's adjustable tool post, patented February 28, 1854. Post Civil War production appears to have limited to steam engines and the firm eventually became the Rollins Engine Co.

ROWLAND, F.C. & A.E., New Haven, CT, later
ROWLAND MACHINE CO., New Haven, CT

    A partnership of Amory E. Rowland (1853-1912) and Frederick C. Rowland (1844-1904), formed in 1877 to make machinists' tools, including engine lathes such as shown at right.
    The firm reorganized as the ROWLAND MACHINE CO. soon after the death of Frederick C. Rowland in 1904.

FIRST CLASS
Machinists' Tools,
F. C. & A. E. ROWLAND,
NEW HAVEN, CONN.

SAN FRANCISCO TOOL CO., San Francisco, CA

Maker of 16" engine lathes in 1883. The lathe had a number of unusual features, including flat carriage ways, outside apron gearing, and outside screws for the tail stock spindles. Perhaps the isolated location, for a machine tool builder, allowed for some original thinking.

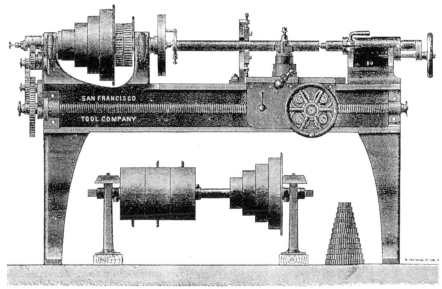

SIXTEEN-INCH SWING LATHE.

SAUNDERS CO., JAMES, Dayton, OH

Maker, in 1907, of the CARROLL attachment for increasing the swing of engine lathes as shown below. "Don't refuse work because your lathe is too small to swing it."

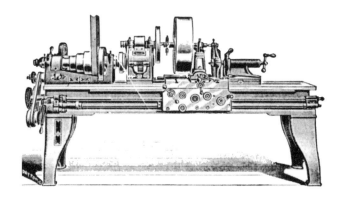

SAWYER WATCH TOOL CO., Fitchburg, MA

Founded July, 1880, by Sylvanus Sawyer as a reorganization of the New England Machine Co. Products offered in 1880 included the No.2 lathe (Fig.1) for watchmakers and the No.2½ (Fig.2) for slightly larger work. The company was active as late as 1901.

No. 2. SAWYER LATHE.

Fig.1

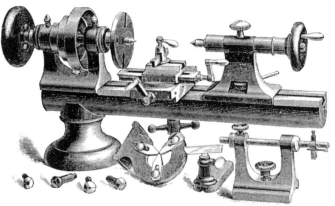

Fig.2

No. 2½ SAWYER LATHE.

SCHUMACHER & BOYE, Cincinnati, OH

A partnership of Ernst A. Schumacher and Frederick W. Boye, formed in 1899 as a reorganization of DIETZ, SCHUMACHER & BOYE. The firm continued to specialize in large engine lathes with swings from 18" to 32" (Fig.1). 28" electrically driven lathes were introduced in 1900 with a variable speed motor mounted in place of the cone pulley (Fig.2). An improved motor drive was offered in 1901 (Fig.3).

1903 production included 18" engine lathes (Fig.4), 20" engine lathes, 26" and 28" engine lathes, 30" and 32" engine lathes, and 36" and 42" engine lathes. All were offered with quick change feed gear boxes, patented August 26 and October 28, 1902, by W.T. Emmes. New design 48" triple geared engine lathes (Fig.5) with quick change feed gear boxes were introduced in 1904.

A second firm, SCUMACHER, BOYE & EMMES, which included William T. Emmes (1863-1928), was also formed in 1899 and also made engine lathes. In 1912 the two firms consolidated as the BOYE & EMMES MACHINE TOOL CO.

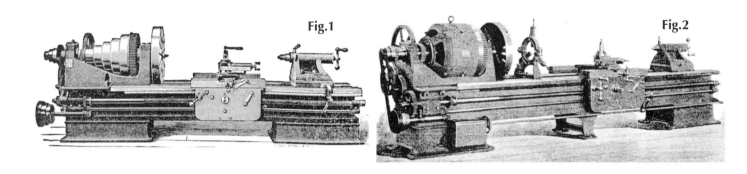

Fig.1

Fig.2

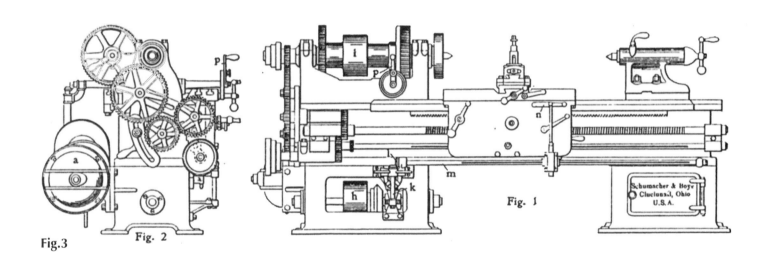

Fig.3

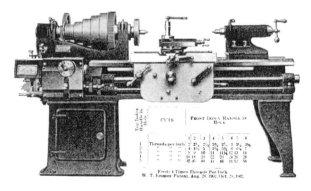

Fig.4

Fig.5

SEBASTIAN LATHE CO., Cincinnati, OH

Formed in 1891 by Benjamin Sebastian, Jr. (1853-1919) and his wife Clara Sebastian. Sebastian was previously a partner in the SEBASTIAN-MAY CO. but sold out in 1891, returned to Cincinnati, and began making foot lathes and engine lathes similar to those made by the SEBASTIAN-MAY CO. In March, 1896, the company moved to a new factory across the river in Covington, KY. Sebastian headed the firm until his retirement in 1917.

Lathes offered in the company's 1893 catalog included 9" and 10" hand or speed lathes (Fig.1), 10" foot-power lathes (Fig.2), 13" foot-power screw cutting lathes (Fig.3), engine lathes in 13", 14", and 15" swings (Fig.4), gap engine lathes in 13/20", 14/21" and 15/22" swings (Fig.5), and 15" back geared turret lathes (Fig.6).

In 1898, the firm offered a gear cutting attachment (Fig.7) that had previously been offered by J.C. PALMER beginning in 1886, and an automatic turret attachment (Fig.8) which could be mounted on its 13" and 15" lathes. All the above products were also offered in its ca.1910 catalog. *(continued on next page)*

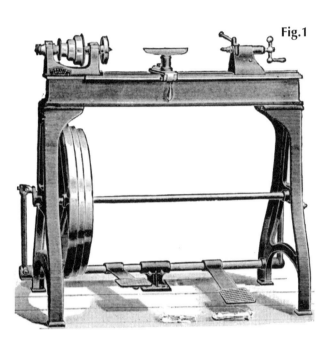

Fig.1

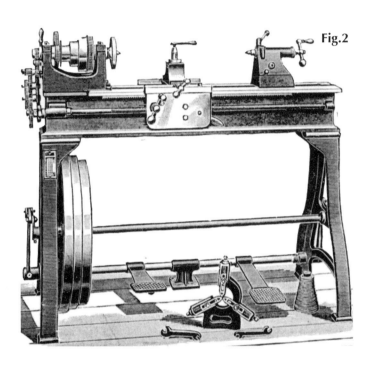

Fig.2

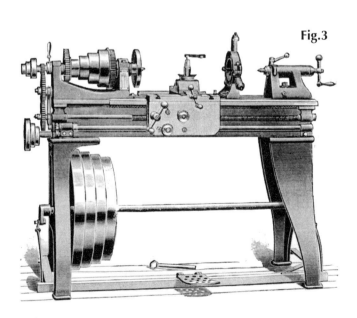

Fig.3

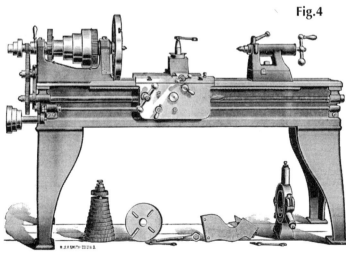

Fig.4

Fig.5

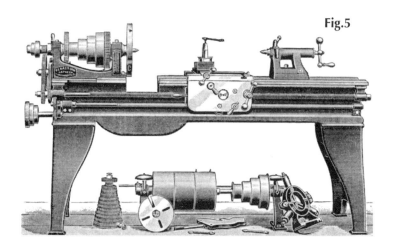

Fig.6

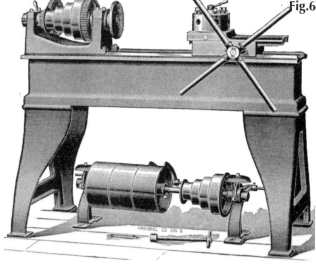

Fig.7

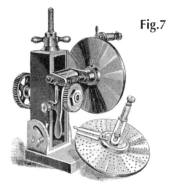

Gear-Cutting Attachment.

Fig.8

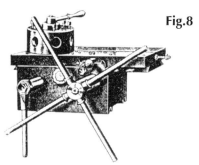

SEBASTIAN-MAY CO., Cincinnati, OH, later Sidney, OH

A partnership of Benjamin Sebastian, Jr. (1853-1919) and Jacob May, formed in 1882 to make small lathes and drill presses. In 1890 the firm moved from Cincinnati to Sidney, OH.

Sebastian sold out to Allen P. Wagner in 1891 and returned to Cincinnati where he founded the SEBASTIAN LATHE CO. May continued the business until mid-1893 when he also sold out to Wagner. He returned to Cincinnati and rejoined his old partner at the SEBASTIAN LATHE CO. Wagner operated under the SEBASTIAN-MAY CO. name until 1898 when he reorganized as the A.P. WAGNER CO.

Products included foot-power lathes offered in 1886 (Fig.1), 18" engine lathes (Fig.2) in 1887, 10" foot-power lathes (Fig.3) in 1890. *(continued on next page)*

Fig.1

NEW ENGINE LATHE.

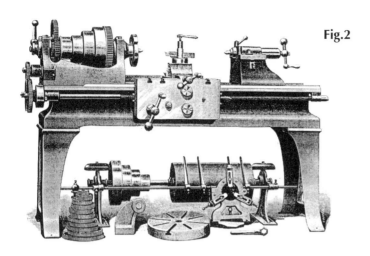
Fig.2

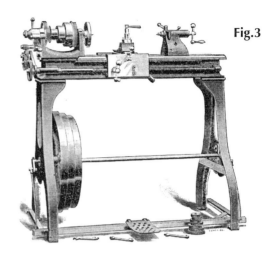
Fig.3

SECOR, JEROME B., Bridgeport, CT

Maker of small turret lathes/screw machines beginning in 1881. Production appears to have ceased about 1890.

NEW SCREW MACHINE.

SELLERS & CO., WILLIAM, Philadelphia, PA

A partnership of William Sellers (1824-1905) and his brother John Sellers, Jr. (1826-1906), formed in 1855 when Edward Bancroft died and the partnership of BANCROFT & SELLERS was reorganized. Their cousin, Coleman Sellers, who had served as superintendent at NILES & CO., joined the firm in 1856 as chief engineer. William Sellers was elected president when the firm incorporated in 1886, serving until his death in 1905.

Production centered around large machine tools for the railroad industry including wheel lathes (Fig.1) introduced in 1860. Lathes offered in their 1877 catalog included axle lathes (Fig.2), 20" chasing lathes (Fig.3), engine lathes from 12" to 72" swing (Figs.4-6), and improved wheel turning lathes (Fig.7). 1884 production included an improved line of engine lathes with swings from 12" to 48" (Figs.8-10), 78" wheel turning lathes with wheel quartering and hub facing attachments (Fig.11), and cylinder boring lathes (Fig.12).

In 1892 Sellers built one of the largest lathes ever made, for turning and boring the new 16" naval guns (Fig.13). *(continued on next two pages)*

SELLERS' IMPROVEMENT IN TURNING LATHES.

Fig.1

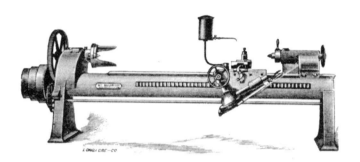

AXLE LATHE.

Fig.2

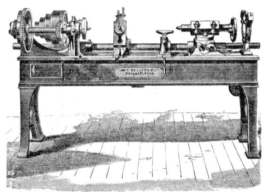

Fig.3

20-INCH CHASING LATHE.

Fig.4

Fig.5

Fig.6

Fig.7

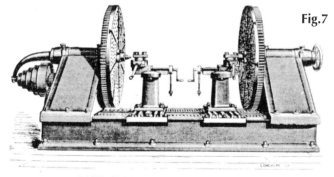

PATENT WHEEL TURNING LATHE.

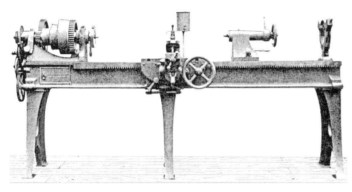

Fig.8

Fig.9

Fig.10

Fig.12

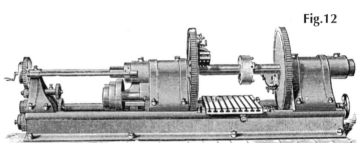

Fig.11

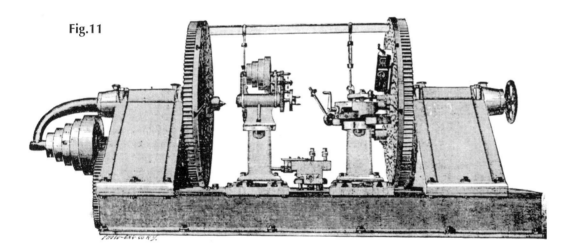

Fig.13

SENECA FALLS MFG. CO., Seneca Falls, NY

Founded in 1879 by Adelbert S. Davis (1847-1924). Davis operated as a proprietorship until 1891 when the firm incorporated with a capital of $60,000. He then served as president until selling the company to Marcus A. Coolidge in 1917. Coolidge merged the company with the FITCHBURG MACHINE WORKS in 1924 and formed the SENECA FALLS MACHINE CO. from the combined companies.

Lathe production began in 1885 with the UNION, 10" foot-power model (Fig.1) that was replaced by the 10" CROWN model (Fig.2) in 1886. A much-improved CROWN new model was introduced by 1901 (Fig.3).

In 1886, the STAR foot-power engine lathe (Fig.4) was introduced in 9" swing only. An 11" model (Fig.5) was added in 1895. By 1898, the STAR line was redesigned, designated the NEW MODEL, and offered in 9" and 11" sizes in foot-power (Fig.6) and countershaft (Fig.7) models. It was also offered in a 13" tool room model with automatic cross-feed (Fig.8) and power cross-feed. Gear cutting (Fig.9), fluting (Fig.10) and milling attachments (Fig.11) for STAR lathes were introduced in 1901.

In 1904 an improved STAR 9" bench lathe (Fig.12) was introduced. Shortly after, a new line of SENECA FALLS engine lathes (Fig.13) was introduced, replacing the STAR line in swings above 11". Equipped with lever change feed, the new SENECA FALLS line was offered in 12", 14" and 16" swings. *(continued on next two pages)*

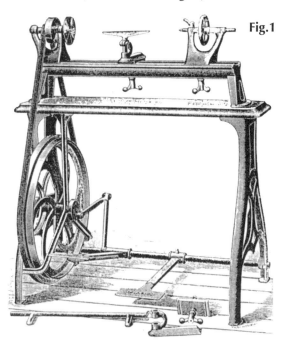
Fig.1

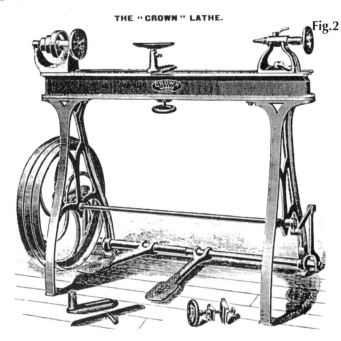
THE "CROWN" LATHE. Fig.2

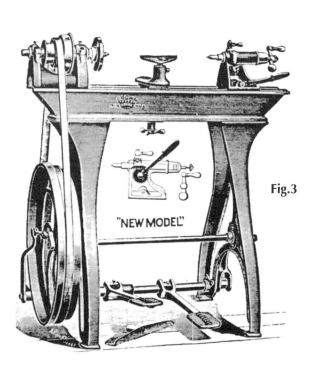
Fig.3 "NEW MODEL"

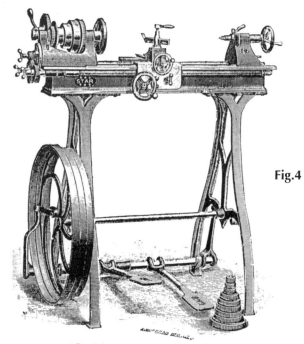
Fig.4
"STAR" SCREW CUTTING ENGINE LATHE.

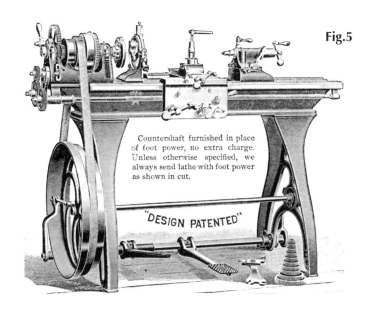

Fig.5

Countershaft furnished in place of foot power, no extra charge. Unless otherwise specified, we always send lathe with foot power as shown in cut.

"DESIGN PATENTED"

Fig.6

"NEW MODEL"

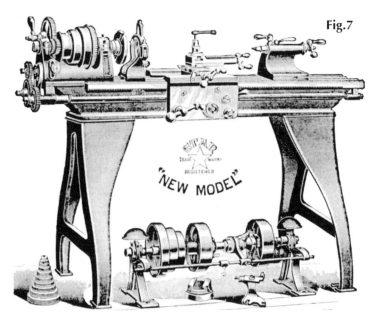

Fig.7

"NEW MODEL"

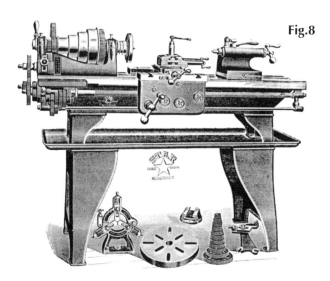

Fig.8

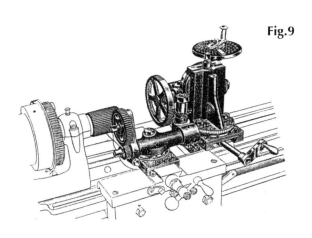

Fig.9

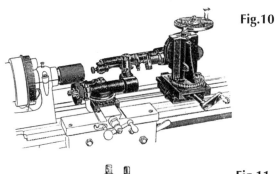

Fig.10

Fig.11

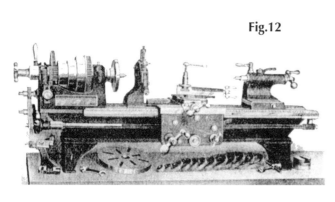

Fig.12

Fig.13

SESSIONS, AREY & CO., Springfield, MA

Maker, in 1864, of engine and hand lathes "of superior quality."

SHANKS, T. , Baltimore, MD

Maker, in 1872, of foot lathes "just the article for sewing machines and shoe factories."

SHAW & LAMBERT, Brockton, MA

A partnership of K.W. Shaw and R.C. Lambert. Maker, in 1882, of lathes and needle machinery.

SHAWMUT LATHE CO., Boston, MA

Included in an 1879 list of machine tool builders. No other information now available.

SHELLENBACK MACHINE TOOL CO., Richmond, IN

Founded in 1891 by Peter Shellenback to make engine lathes, jointly patented February 17, 1891, with William Shellenback. Production included the 24" model shown below. In 1894, Shellenback moved to Liberty, IN, and consolidated his lathe line with that of the LIBERTY MFG. CO.

Shellenback had also been the proprietor of the RICHMOND CITY MILL WORKS, maker of the SHELLENBACK pulley lathe, until selling out in 1890. (See HENLEY MACHINE TOOL WORKS.)

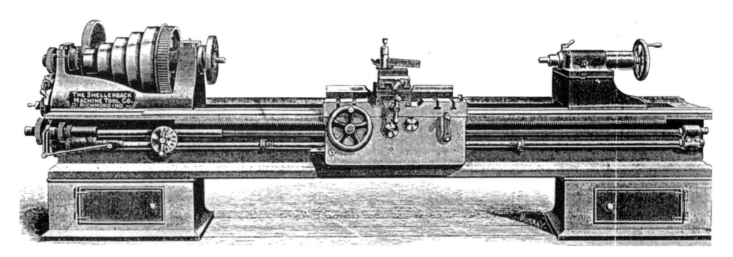

SHEPARD & CO., H.L., Cincinnati, OH, later
SHEPARD LATHE CO., Cincinnati, OH

Founded in 1875 by H.L. Shepard to make foot lathes and other light machine tools. By 1881, however, he was offering 20" engine lathes (Fig.1). His 1882 catalog offered a variety of foot-power lathes included an 8" model (Fig.2) that was also made in a bench model with countershaft drive (Fig.3), a 6" bench lathe (Fig.4), and a 14" foot-power lathe (Fig.5).

The firm reorganized as the SHEPARD LATHE CO. when Shepard retired in 1898 and his son took over the business. Products offered in 1900 included lathes in several types and sizes (Fig.6). Production of light duty lathes continued as late as 1921. *(continued on next page)*

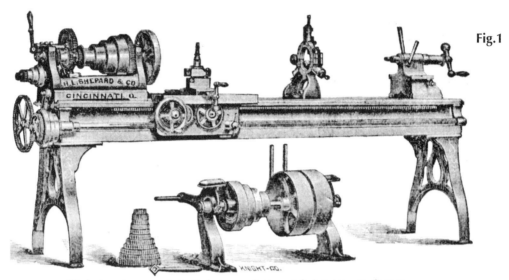

20 inch swing over Bed, 14 inch over Rest, and 8 feet between Centres.

Fig.1

New 8x25 Inch Back Geared Screw Cutting Lathes.
PRICE, $90.00.

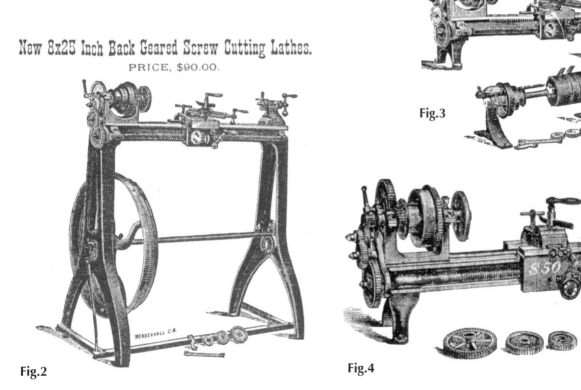

Fig.2

Fig.3

Fig.4

SHEPARD'S $60 BENCH ENGINE LATHE.

Fig.5

Fig.6

SHEPARD, LATHE & CO., Worcester, MA

A partnership of Russell R. Shepard, Martin Lathe, and Edwin Morse, formed in 1853 as successor to S.C. COOMBS & CO. Maker of a variety of machine tools including the 20" swing lathe shown below. The firm reorganized as LATHE & MORSE when Shepard left in 1864.

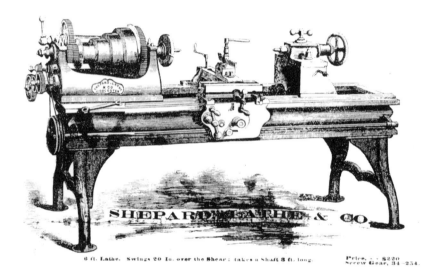

SIGOURNEY TOOL CO., Hartford, CT

Formed about 1882 to made 10" hand lathes and light drilling machines as shown below. The firm's main product was the line of light drilling machines offered until about 1929.

SILK, P.P., Cincinnati, OH, later
SILK, ANDERSON & CO., Cincinnati, OH

Formed in 1897 by P.P. Silk when he left the SMITH & SILK MACHINE TOOL CO. to begin making 12" and 14" engine lathes (Fig.1).

In 1898 Silk formed a partnership with Lars W. Anderson and reorganized as SILK, ANDERSON & CO., which offered engine lathes in 16", 18" and 20" swings (Fig.2).

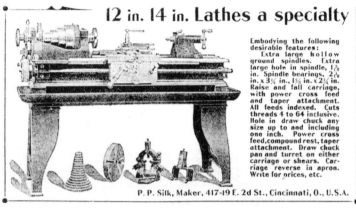

Fig.1

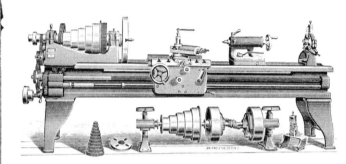

Fig.2

SILVER & GAY, North Chelmsford, MA, later
SILVER & GAY CO.. North Chelmsford, MA

A partnership of Harvey Silver (?-1884) and Ziba Gay, Jr. (1823-1902) formed in 1857 as a reorganization of GAY, SILVER & CO. In 1884, the firm reorganized as the SILVER & GAY CO.

Products included textile machinery, lathes, planers and other machine tools. Machine tool production, however, ceased before 1901.

SLOAN & CO., C.T., Newark, NJ, later
SLOAN, CHACE & CO., Newark, NJ, later
SLOAN & CHACE MFG. CO., Newark, NJ

Founded by Charles T. Sloan about 1875. In 1886 the firm reorganized as SLOAN, CHACE & CO., a partnership of Charles T. Sloan and George E.O. Chace. By 1906, the firm became the SLOAN & CHACE MFG. CO. All three firms made small bench lathes.

Products included 8" machinist's bench lathes (Fig.1) offered in 1885 and 7" precision bench lathes (Fig.2) offered in 1906. Screw cutting attachments (Fig.3) were available which, with a set of 25 change gears, could cut threads from 14 to 200 per inch. A combination 50 tooth and 127 tooth gear was furnished to translate inches to centimeters. *(continued on next page)*

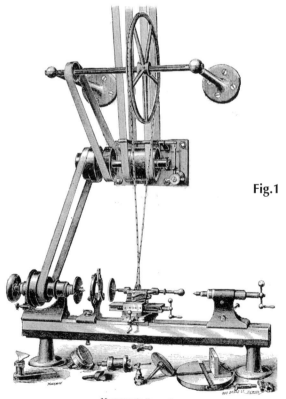

Fig.1

MACHINIST'S BENCH LATHE.

Fig.2

SLOAN & CHACE MANUFACTURING CO., Ltd.

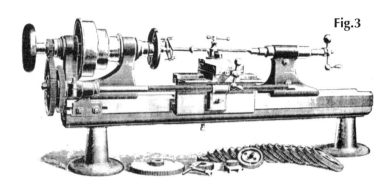

Fig.3

SMITH & GARVIN, New York, NY

Founded in 1862 by Hugh R. Garvin. The firm reorganized in 1879 as E.E. GARVIN & CO. Products in 1873 included drill presses, milling machines and small lathes.

SMURR & KAMEN MACHINE CO., Chicago, IL

A partnership of Napoleon Smurr and John F. Kamen formed about 1907 to make small turret lathes/screw machines such as those shown at left. The firm appears to have ceased operations soon after 1920.

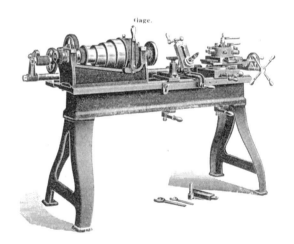

SNYDER & METCALF, Watertown, NY

Formed in 1896 to take over the lathe business of the GAGE MACHINE WORKS. The new firm continued to make GAGE lathes as late as 1905, including the 15" brass finisher's monitor lathe shown at right.

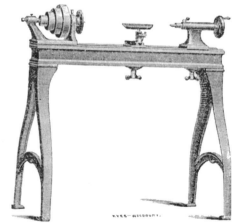

Fig.1

THE SPENCER LATHE.

SPENCER, J.E., Worcester, MA, later
SPENCER & BROWNELL, Worcester, MA

John E. Spencer, who claimed to have begun in 1862, made a line of small lathes equipped with "shell bearings," which he patented April 21, 1874. An existing 8" foot-power lathe is equipped with a threading mechanism utilizing threaded mandrels, one for each thread pitch to be cut.

By 1881, the firm was operating as a partnership of David Spencer, probably J.E. Spencer's son, and George L. Brownell. The new firm continued to advertise that its lathes were equipped with Spencer patented "shell bearings." (*Fig. at left. Continued on next page*)

Spencer & Brownell products included light duty 11", 12" and 14" hand lathes (Fig.1), with an optional slide rest (Fig.2), and 8" bench lathes (Fig.3). All were offered as late as 1897.

Fig.2

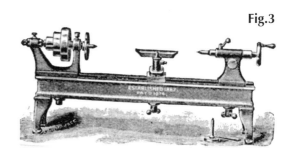

Fig.3

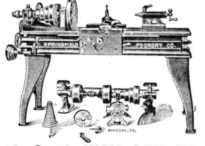

12 & 13 INCH LATHES
BUILT BY
THE SPRINGFIELD FOUNDRY CO.,
Send for
circular **SPRINGFIELD, OHIO, U.S.A.**

SPRINGFIELD FOUNDRY CO., Springfield, OH

Operated jointly with the FAIRBANKS MACHINE TOOL CO., both firms were managed by John G. Sadlier (1856-1902). Maker, in 1900, of 12" and 13" engine lathes.

SPRINGFIELD MACHINE TOOL CO., Springfield, OH

Founded in 1887 by Phillip E. Montanus (1854-1932), William H. Owen (?-1906) and Frank Kempsmith (1848-1904) to make lathes under contract for LODGE, DAVIS & CO. Montanus served as president until his death in 1932. Owen left in 1893 to found the OWEN MACHINE TOOL CO. Kempsmith left in 1888 to found the KEMPSMITH MACHINE TOOL CO.

In 1891, the firm incorporated with a capital of $50,000 and began offering hand and power presses under its own name.

Edward A. Muller, who had been superintendent of LODGE & DAVIS MACHINE TOOL CO., joined the firm as superintendent in 1894. Muller designed a new engine lathe, introduced in late 1894 as the SPRINGFIELD-MULLER lathe (Fig.1) in 18" swing only. Other new lathe designs, 18" cabinet style universal monitor lathes (Fig.2), and 14" FOX hand lathes, were introduced in 1895. *(continued on next page)*

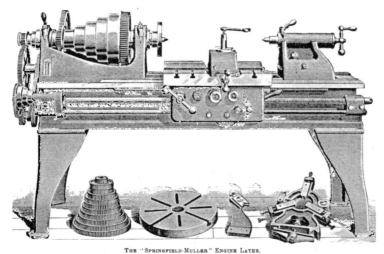

THE "SPRINGFIELD-MULLER" ENGINE LATHE.

Fig.1

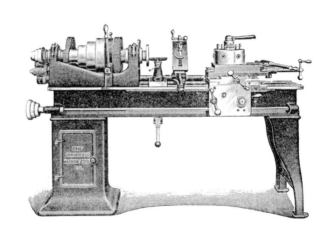

Fig.2

In 1901, the Muller-designed IDEAL engine lathe (Fig.3) was introduced. Equipped with a revolving magazine for feed change gears, it was offered in 14", 16" and 18" swings. By 1904 IDEAL lathes could also be ordered fitted with DC motors and a variable speed control (Fig.4).

1905 production included 24" combination turret lathes (Fig.5) and 18" engine lathes with a turret mounted on a special carriage (Fig.6).

Cabinet style universal turret lathes were available in a motor driven version (Fig.7) by 1908. The newly designed 19" heavy duty "Rapid Reduction" lathe was also offered with motor drive in 1908.

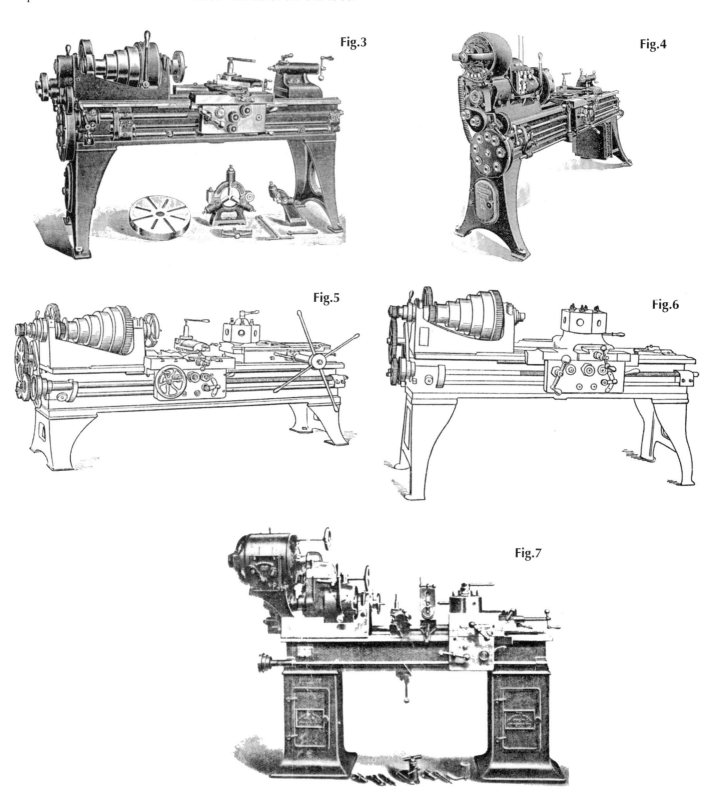

Fig.3

Fig.4

Fig.5

Fig.6

Fig.7

SPRINGFIELD TOOL CO., Springfield, MA

Operated by Chester Van Horn. Maker, c1855-1860, of 14" engine lathes equipped with Van Horns' tool elevator, patented April 17, 1855. The lathes were offered with 7', 10', and 13' beds, longer than normal for the swing.

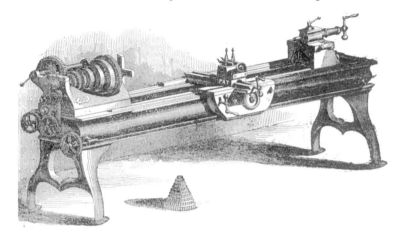

STANDARD MACHINE WORKS, Camden, NJ

Maker, in 1883, of Gray's patent screw machines and engine lathes.

STAR TOOL CO., Providence, RI

Maker, c1875-1885, of a variety of machine tools, including 13", 15", 16" and 18" engine lathes (Fig.1), and drilling lathes offered in 1876. Improved 20" engine lathes (Fig.2) were offered in 1884.

Fig.1

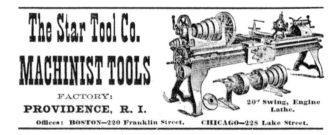

Fig.2

STARK TOOL CO., Waltham, MA

Founded May 1, 1862, by John Stark to make small lathes and other machinery for the watch industry. Stark served as president until his death about 1900. His son John Stark, Jr. then took over the firm, operating as proprietor until incorporation in 1918.

Early production centered around watchmakers' lathes patented May 30, 1865, reissued October 19, 1872, (Fig.1).

Lathes offered in its 1902 catalog included the No.3, 7" turret lathe (Fig.2), No.4, 9" turret lathe (Fig.3), and the No.4 lathe with gear cutting attachment (Fig.4). 1904 production included No.3, 7" and No.4, 9" chasing lathes (Fig.5) and a grinding attachment for No.3 and No.4 lathes (Fig.6). *(continued on next page)*

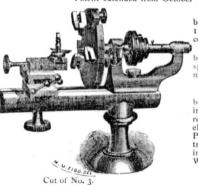

Stark's New Patent Combination Lathes.

Patent extended from October 19, 1872.

No. 1. STEEL; small, 6¾ in. bed, with 9 chucks, viz: 5 split, 1 cement, 1 Patent cement, 1 centre, 1 step.   Price $36.00

No. 2. STEEL; large, 8¼ in. bed, with ten chucks, viz.: 5 split, 1 cement, 1 Patent cement, 1 centre, 2 step.
Price $39.00

No. 3. STEEL; large, 8½ in. bed, with Universal head, 4 inches in diam.—Patent slide rest, that works with cutters; eleven chucks, viz : 5 split, 1 Patent cement, 1 stud, 1 centre, and 3 step the whole forming a complete Lathe for Watchmakers' use.
Price $120.00

Cut of No. 3.

Fig.1

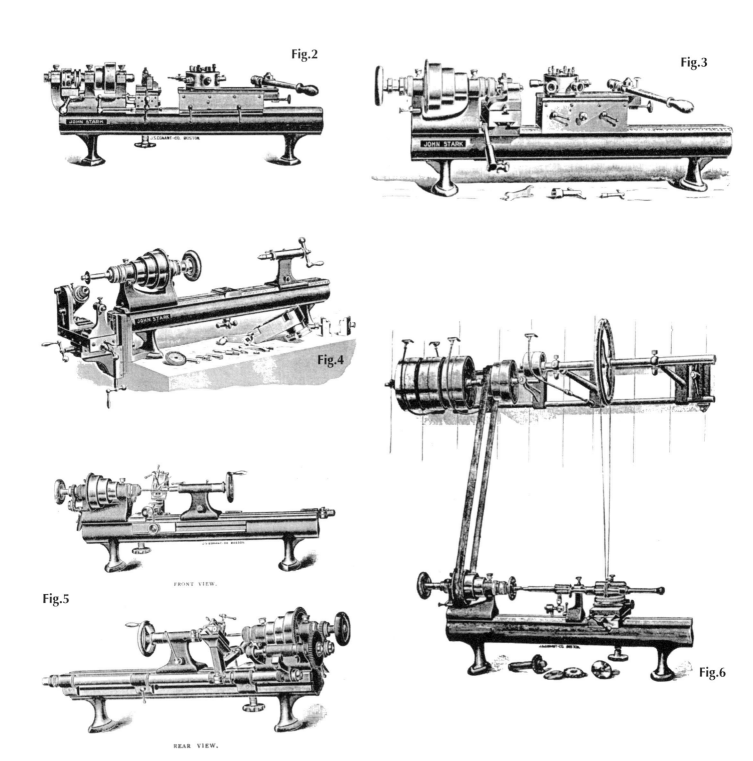

Fig.2

Fig.3

Fig.4

Fig.5

FRONT VIEW.

REAR VIEW.

Fig.6

STATE & CO., R.L., Springfield, OH

Maker, in 1876, of Gardiner's centering and squaring attachment for lathes, patented December 4, 1866, by Charles O. Gardiner. The firm claimed a production of 70" of shafting per hour when using their attachment.

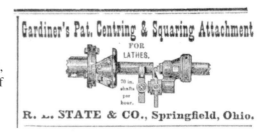

STEINLE TURRET MACHINE CO., Madison, WI

Founded in 1907 by George A. Steinle (1865-1939) and his brother Joseph E. A sister, Katherine and another brother Leo C. were also associated with the company. The firm's sole product appears to have been heavy turret lathes developed by George A. Steinle who had been employed by the GISHOLT MACHINE CO.

Introduced in 1907, the 22" heavy turret lathe (Fig.1) was offered with a geared head, power feed for both carriages, and a tool post side carriage designed to run past the chuck. The latter feature allowed the turret to come very close to the chuck and therefore reduce tool overhang. An improved model (Fig.2) was introduced by 1910.

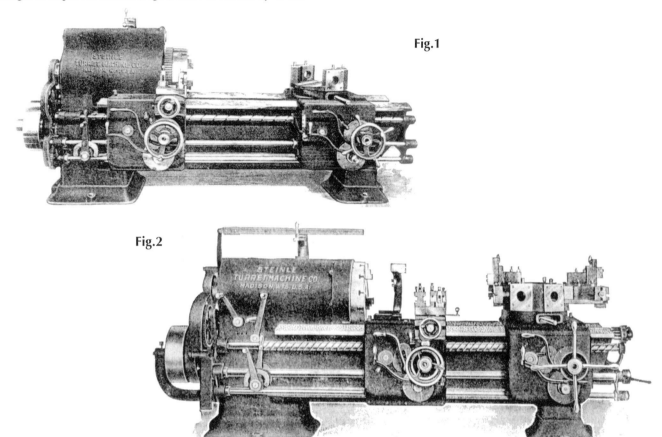

Fig.1

Fig.2

STEPTOE, McFARLAN & CO., Cincinnati, OH

A partnership of John Steptoe (1804-1888) and Thomas McFarlan, formed in 1860. The firm failed in 1878 and was reorganized as John Steptoe & Co. Steptoe is credited with being one of the first machine tool builders in Cincinnati.

Woodworking machinery was the bulk of its business at first, although the firm reportedly offered a copy of the Putnam engine lathe in the 1860s. By 1870 Steptoe employed 300 hands and production included metalworking lathes, planers, radial drills, shapers and slotters. Advertisements claimed "we employ none but the best workmen."

STOCKMAR & DUVINAGE, New York, NY

A partnership of Alexander Stockmar and Lewis Duvinage, formed about 1862 to make engine lathes. The firm was dissolved in 1868.

STONE & HAZELTON, Boston, MA

A partnership of J.F. Stone and Frederick Hazelton. Maker of engine lathes c1876-1882. In 1879, the firm introduced Hazelton's patent combination turning and screw tool for engine lathes, shown at right.

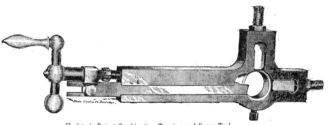

Hazelton's Patent Combination Turning and Screw Tool.

STREIT & SON, A., Cincinnati, OH, later
STREIT MACHINE CO., A., Cincinnati, OH

Founded by Anton Streit in 1892 to make 36" boring lathes (Fig.1) and Streit patent 26" pulley lathes (Fig.2) that could cut straight- or crown face- pulleys.

By 1898 the firm had reorganized as the A. STREIT MACHINE CO., which in 1903 introduced improved versions of both the boring lathe and pulley lathe. In 1907, the line was sold to the newly formed Cincinnati Pulley Machinery Co., which continued production.

THE STREIT BORING MACHINE.   **Fig.1**

Fig.2

STROUD WORKS, Middletown, CT

Operated by William Stroud, machine tool production began about 1850. Products included a Howe type turret lathe designed in 1857-1858. At least one lot of 25 was made for sale in 1861.

SWISHER, L.C., Coffeyville, KS

Maker of the Swisher Automatic Boring and Turning Lathe, introduced in 1892. Swisher claimed the machine was "designed for use in boring, mortising, shaping, turning, screw cutting, milling, planing and rifling."

The machine was equipped with a two-axis worktable (C in drawing at right) with two vises (one swivel, one stationary), which allowed for the boring, mortising, shaping, milling, planing and rifling functions.

As with most multi-function machines, it was probably too complex to be successful. However, it shows a good deal of ingenuity and must have appealed to gunsmiths, repair shops, etc.

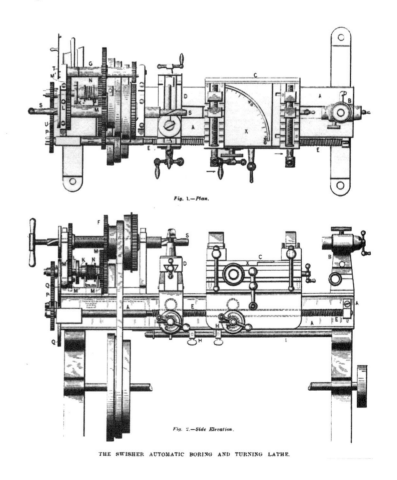

Fig. 1.—Plan.

Fig. 2.—Side Elevation.

THE SWISHER AUTOMATIC BORING AND TURNING LATHE.

THAYER, A. & S., Worcester, MA, later
THAYER, HOUGHTON & CO., Worcester, MA

A partnership of Alexander Thayer (1812-1895) and Sewell Thayer formed in 1845 to make lathes and other machine tools. The firm reorganized as THAYER, HOUGHTON & CO. in 1853 when Sewell Thayer died and was replaced by Hannibal H. Houghton (1827-1898) and E.C. Cleveland.

In 1854, the firm was burned out in the Merrifield Building fire. Within a year the partners built the WASHINGTON ST. MACHINE SHOP and continued production of "engine, hand, chucking and wood lathes" as well as a variety of other machine tools as shown in the ad below.

In 1862, the partners sold out to the NEW YORK STEAM ENGINE WORKS, which continued production at the Worcester factory. Alexander Thayer stayed on as superintendent until he left in 1864 to join the NEW HAVEN MFG. CO.

WASHINGTON ST. MACHINE SHOP,
THAYER, HOUGHTON & CO., PROPRIETORS,
MANUFACTURERS OF
MACHINISTS' TOOLS,
of SUPERIOR QUALITY; such as
IRON PLANERS, ENGINE, HAND, CHUCKING & WOOD LATHES,
Bolt Cutters, Upright and Swing Drills,
BORING MACHINES, & BORING MILLS, for Car Wheels and Mill work,
SLABBING MACHINES, &c., &c.
Also, JOB WORK of all kinds, including Shafting, Pulleys and Hangers, Long Screws, Iron Planing, Gear Cutting, &c. Patent Chucks always on hand at Manufacturers' Prices.
Address as above,
Worcester, Mass.

THOMAS IRON WORKS, Worcester, MA

Founded by Alfred Thomas in 1864 to make 17", 20" and 22", heavy engine lathes patented by Thomas March 6, 1866, and November 5, 1867. The business failed in 1870.

This machine, being the LATEST pattern out, has a combination of patents and improvements not used on any other machine, and for power, simplicity, durability, workmanship and convenience, is unsurpassed by anything of its kind. For this and other machinists' tools, send for circular, to
THOMAS IRON WORKS, No. 5 CYPRESS ST., WORCESTER, MASS.

THOMPSON, FRANK, New York, NY

Maker, in 1882, of "Monitor, Hand, Speed and Back Geared Lathes. Slide Rests, Chucks and Brass Finishers' Tools of the finest quality".

THOMPSON, SKINNER & CO., Worcester, MA

A partnership of Elijah Thompson and Franklin Skinner, formed in 1845 to make machinery and machine tools, including lathes. The firm was absorbed by the NEW HAVEN MFG. CO. in 1853.

THOMPSON, WILLIAM, Worcester, MA

Maker, in 1856, of blacksmiths' shears and "lathes built to order." Thompson was operating as late as 1868 when he received a patent for a lathe tool post.

TODD & CO., JAMES, Cincinnati, OH

Listed in an 1851 directory as employing 50 hands making steam engines, planers and lathes.

TOLMAN & CO., C.S., Fitchburg, MA, later
TOLMAN, C.S., Fitchburg, MA, later

A partnership of Cyrus S. Tolman and Asher Green, listed in the 1855 city directory as a maker of planers, engine lathes and hand lathes. Tolman's 1865 listing showed him operating as C.S. TOLMAN, maker of engine and hand lathes.

Tolman worked for the New England Vise Co. from 1871 to 1873. In 1873, he resumed making hand lathes, operating as C.S. TOLMAN. Engine lathes were added in 1878, but lathe production was discontinued in 1887 to concentrate on grinding machinery.

TOTTEN & HOGG IRON and STEEL FOUNDRY CO., Pittsburgh, PA

An important maker of steel rolling mill machinery, the firm, in 1892, introduced a line of STANDARD roll lathes for users who wanted to make their own rolls.

The roll lathes were offered in 55" swing with 18' bed (shown below), 38" swing with 18' bed, and 24" swing with 18' bed. The steps in the five-step cone were six inches wide.

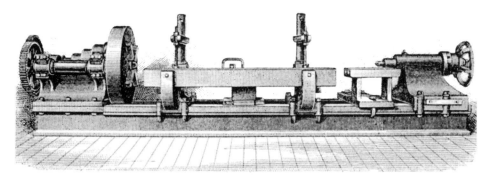

STANDARD ROLL LATHE.

TWISS, PRATT & HAYES, New Haven, CT, later
TWISS, HAYES & CO., New Haven, CT

Formed about 1867 to make lathes, screw machines, shapers, and planers. The firm reorganized as TWISS, HAYES & CO. in 1869.

UNION WORKS, South Boston, MA

Founded about 1848 by Seth Wilmarth (1810-1886) who remained the proprietor until his death. The firm designed and made very large lathes (up to 15' swing x 50' bed) and planers (up to 10' x 60') for the Boston Navy Yard and others.

UNIVERSAL RADIAL DRILL CO., Cincinnati, OH

Founded in 1879 by Charles Hoefinghoff (1833-1899) and George A. Gray, Jr. (1839-1905) to make a line of radial drilling machines. Gray left the firm in 1881 to found G.A. GRAY, JR. & CO. In 1886, Hoefinghoff sold out to Perrin G. March (1853-1930) who operated it until 1898 when he sold the company to the BICKFORD DRILL & TOOL CO.

In addition to the line of radial drills, the firm offered, in 1891, 25" turret lathes (Fig.1), 30" turret chucking lathes (Fig.2) and double-ended facing lathes (Fig.3). *(continued on next page)*

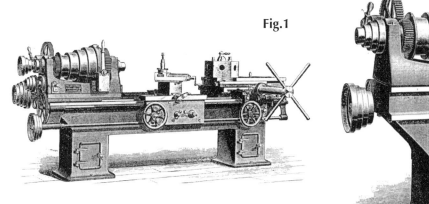

Fig.1

Fig.2

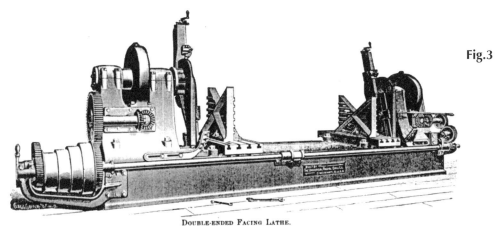

Fig.3

DOUBLE-ENDED FACING LATHE.

VON WYCK MACHINE TOOL CO., Cincinnati, OH

Formed in 1903 as the successor to the ROACH & VON WYCK MACHINE TOOL CO. Emil Von Wyck (1865-1912) was president. In 1915 the company was taken over by the Cisco Machine Tool Co.

15" engine lathes (Fig.1) were offered in 1903. An improved version with a quick change feed gear box (Fig.2) was introduced in 1908.

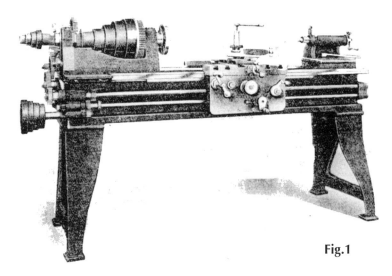

Fig.1

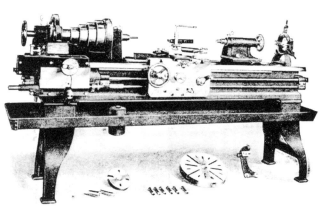

Fig.2

WAGNER CO., A.P., Sidney, OH, later Detroit, MI

Formed in 1898 by Allen P. Wagner. With a $25,000 loan from his cousin's husband, Ignatius H. Thedieck, Wagner had purchased lathe maker SEBASTIAN-MAY CO. in 1891. In 1898, he renamed it and moved to Detroit, MI. In 1909, Thedieck took control of the firm, moved it back to Sidney and renamed it the MONARCH MACHINE CO.

WALCOTT & SON, GEORGE D., Jackson, MI, later
WALCOTT & WOOD MACHINE TOOL CO., Jackson, MI

A partnership of George D. Walcott and his son Edward A. Walcott (1860-1904) formed in 1881. George Walcott's daughters, Martha C. and Caroline L., with Erwin E. Wood, reorganized the firm as the WALCOTT & WOOD MACHINE TOOL CO. in 1907.

Though best known for shapers, products also included 22" engine lathes offered in 1883 (Fig.1) and an improved model (Fig.2) introduced in 1890. A newly designed 16" engine lathe with a quick-change feed gear box (Fig.3) was introduced in 1908.

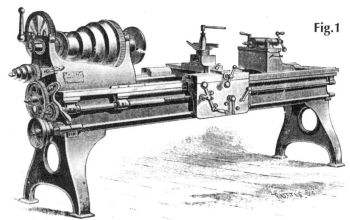

Fig.1

Fig.2

Fig.3

WALTHAM MACHINE WORKS, Waltham, MA

Formed in 1898 as a partnership of Edmund L. Sanderson and Benjamin F. Ellis to make small lathes and other small machine tools for the Waltham watch industry. The firm expanded in 1902 by taking over the factory of the ALCORN & AMES CO. Products included 8" bench lathes introduced in 1908 (at right).

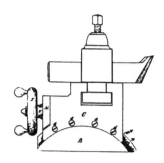

WALTHAM WATCH TOOL CO., Waltham, MA

Formed in 1885 as a reorganization of the HOPKINS WATCH TOOL CO. The organizers were Caleb Hopkins Van Norman, founder of the HOPKINS WATCH TOOL CO. and his sons Edmund F. (?-1890) and Frederick D. (1862-1963). A third son, Charles E. (1859-1946) joined in 1888.

Early products were aimed at watchmakers, but larger bench lathes were offered by 1890. These VAN NORMAN 7"x 28" lathes (Fig.1) were offered with attachments for threading (Fig.2), milling (Fig.3), and gear cutting (Fig.4).

The firm reorganized as the VAN NORMAN MACHINE TOOL CO. in 1912.

Fig.1

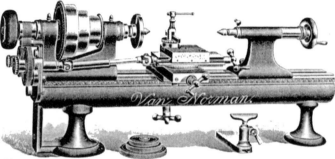

Fig.2

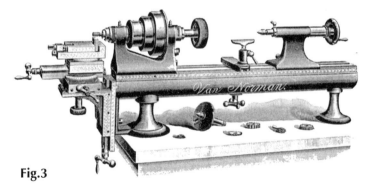

Fig.3

Fig.4

WARNER & SWASEY, Chicago, IL, later Cleveland, OH, later
WARNER & SWASEY CO., Cleveland, OH

A partnership of Worcester R. Warner (1846-1929) and Ambrose Swasey (1846-1937) formed in 1880. Both partners had been apprentices at the EXETER MACHINE WORKS and both joined the PRATT & WHITNEY CO. in 1870 where they worked as contracting foremen.

The firm moved to Cleveland, OH, in 1882, probably due to an order for 140 machines placed by a Lorain, OH, brass company. In 1900, the partners incorporated, with a capital of $500,000, as the WARNER & SWASEY CO.

Early products centered around brassworking machines and included 16" monitor lathes (Fig.1) offered in 1883, double head brassworkers' lathes (Fig.2) offered in 1890, offset lathes (Fig.3) offered in 1892, and 24" universal monitor lathes introduced in 1893 (Fig.4). Smaller size FOX universal monitor lathes (Fig.5) were available by 1895.

In 1899, the now famous 2"x 24" "Hollow Hexagon" turret lathe (Fig.6) was introduced. A line of turret screw machines was introduced in 1900 and included No.1, 5/8", No.2, 1", No.4, 1½" (Fig.7), No.6, 2 1/8" and No.8, 3 5/8" sizes. *(continued on next page)*

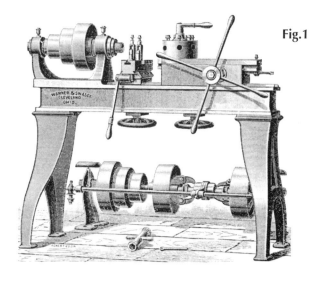

Fig.1

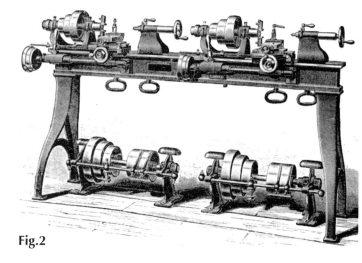

Fig.2

Fig.3

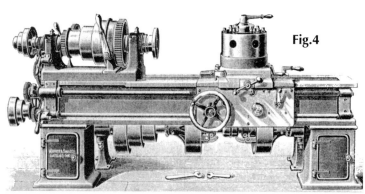

Fig.4

Fig.5

WARNER & SWASEY,
CLEVELAND, OHIO.
MANUFACTURERS OF
UNIVERSAL MONITORS.
IRON AND BRASS WORKING MACHINERY.
SEND FOR ILLUSTRATED CATALOGUE.

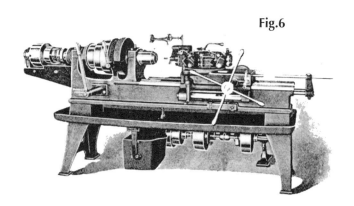

Fig.6

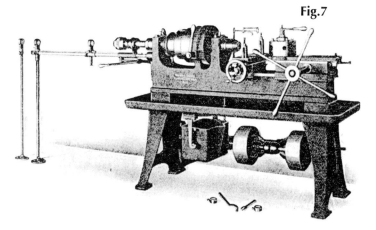

Fig.7

WARNER, WHITNEY & CO., Nashua, NH

A partnership of David A.G. Warner and George Whitney, formed as a reorganization of GAGE, WARNER & WHITNEY when John H. Gage died in 1872.

Products included locomotive driving wheel lathes such as shown in the c1875 stereoptican print shown below.

**Photo courtesy of
Robert Vogel**

WARWICK TOOL CO., Middletown, CT

Formed about 1865 to make small tools. In 1867 the firm introduced the PARKER gear cutting attachment for engine lathes, patented July 3, 1866, (Fig.1) and an associated attachment for fluting reamers, splining studs, etc. (Fig.2).

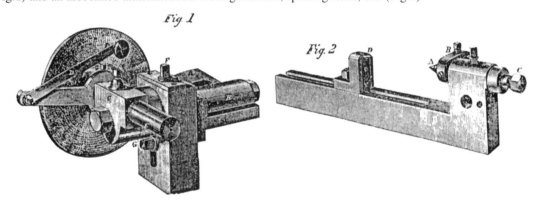

WASHBURN MACHINE SHOP, Worcester, MA

Operated by the Worcester Free Institute, a technical school for boys. Milton P. Higgins (1842-1912) served as superintendent from 1869 to 1896.

The shop offered a number of products, made by the students, for sale to industry. Lathe production began by 1872 or before and included the 16" swing model, shown below, into the 1880s. *(continued on next page)*

Lathe: 16 inch Swing, 8 ft. Bed.

WATERBURY FARREL FOUNDRY & MACHINE CO., Waterbury, CT

Formed in 1880 by Edward C. Lewis (1826-1901) when he bought the Waterbury, CT, factory of the Farrel Foundry & Machine Co. Lewis served as president until his death in 1901. His son-in-law, William S. Fulton, served as president from 1901 until his retirement in 1919.

The company made a variety of metal-forming machinery including, in 1884, hand spinning lathes (Fig.1), the very complex SEYMOUR'S spinning lathe (Fig.2) patented in 1868, 1873, and 1874, and edging lathes (Fig.3) "for trimming the irregular edges of every description of metallic shells."

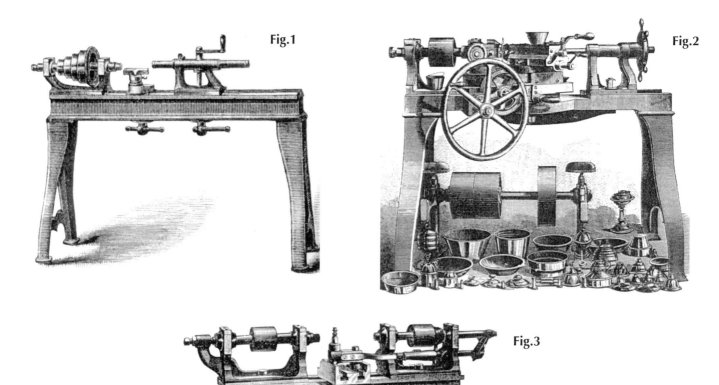

Fig.1

Fig.2

Fig.3

EDGING LATHE.

WATERHOUSE ELECTRIC AND MFG. CO., Hartford, CT

Maker, in 1886, of a 7" swing bench lathe (Fig.1) and a larger Universal engine lathe (Fig.2). The designs appear to have been taken over from the BALLOU MFG. CO., which failed in 1886.

Fig.1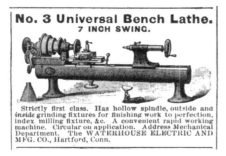

Fig.2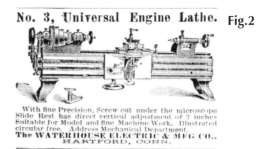

WATSON, JAMES, Philadelphia, PA

Maker, in 1877, of a 30" swing gap lathe with a 21' bed. Note the hand-operated crane for loading workpieces.

WATSON'S GAP LATHE.

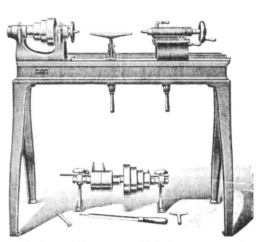

WELLS & SON CO., F.E., Greenfield, MA

A partnership of Frederick E. Wells (1844-1936) and his son Frederick W. Wells (1881-1946) formed in 1890. Lathes were not primary products, but beginning about 1905 the company offered a line of 11" speed lathes as shown at right. The firm was consolidated with GREENFIELD TAP & DIE CO. in 1916.

For Pattern Makers, Ameteur Mechanics or anyone wanting a strictly high grade lathe. Used in the largest and most up-to-date machine and woodworking shops.

Lathe with 4 ft. bed, 11 in. swing, 9-16 hole in sqindle,
Price, $48.00

WHEELER & CO., J.S., Worcester, MA

A partnership of Joshua S. Wheeler, Asa N. Wheeler and Orange Wheeler, formed in 1867 to make lathes, planers, upright drills, milling machines, and other machine tools. The firm operated until 1905.

Lathes produced after 1871 (Fig.1) were equipped with an adjustable tool rest (Fig.2), jointly patented by the three partners on June 27, 1871.

Fig.1

Fig.2

WHEELER, WILLIAM A., Worcester, MA

Founded in 1823 when Wheeler established the first foundry in Worcester. In 1836, the firm employed 25 men, turning out 700,000 pounds of castings annually. Machine tool production began about 1835 and, by 1840, Wheeler had ten men building wooden bed, chain feed lathes similar to that shown below. Production continued until Wheeler's death in 1867.

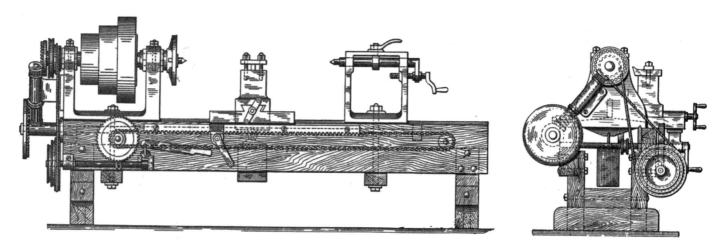

WHITCOMB & CO. C., Worcester, MA, later
WHITCOMB MFG. CO., Worcester, MA

A partnership of Carter Whitcomb and his brother Alonzo Whitcomb (1818-1900) formed in 1849 to make chain drive engine lathes and planers. Lathe production appears to have ceased prior to 1876 when the firm began to specialize in planers.

In 1881, Carter Whitcomb left and Alonzo Whitcomb merged the firm with RICE & WHITCOMB to form the WHITCOMB MFG. CO. Alonzo Whitcomb, Jr. (1862-1936) took over when his father died in 1900, operating the firm until 1905 when he merged with P. BLAISDELL & CO. to form the WHITCOMB-BLAISDELL MACHINE TOOL CO. *(continued on next page)*

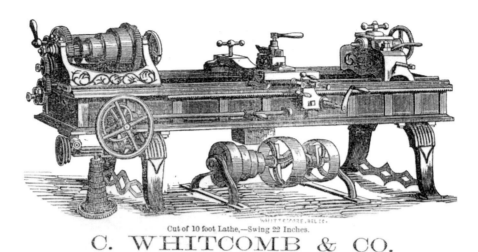

Cut of 10 foot Lathe,—Swing 22 Inches.

C. WHITCOMB & CO.

WHITE, J.D., New Haven, CT

Maker, in 1852, of taper turning engine lathes, patented May 21, 1850, and double end railway axle lathes.

WHITIN & SON, P., Whitinsville, MA

Operator of a large machine shop making textile machinery, the firm also made a variety of small machine tools for the New England firearms industry during the Civil War. Production is believed to include lathes and milling machines.

The firm also made, in 1864-1865, a "lathe attachment for centering and squaring," patented January 29, 1861, by N.F. Newell. The device consisted of a foot-operated, two jaw clamp which centered the workpiece, and a combination center drilling and facing tool which rotated in the lathe spindle. Feeding the workpiece towards the spindle would square the end and drill a center hole.

The parts marked X in the illustration below are a system that fed cutting oil to the tool, prevented it from splashing out of the machine, and then recovered both the oil and chips. This may be the earliest example of such a complete system.

WHITNEY, BAXTER D., Winchendon, MA

Whitney (1817-1915), in 1833, designed and built an 18" engine lathe with several advanced features as shown below. Construction was all cast iron except for two wooden beams running between the legs; back gears were mounted under the head; and smooth feed was generated by a worm and large worm wheel drive through a rack attached to the tool carriage. *(continued on next page)*

The lathe appears to have been still in use when found by E.A. Dixie in 1908. Dixie, who had been surveying New England for old machine tools, photographed the machine for an article which appeared in "American Machinist" magazine, February 27, 1908.

WHITNEY, GEORGE H., Nashua, NH

Maker, in 1881, of heavy engine lathes for railroad use.

WHITTELSEY, C.C., Malone, NY

Founded in 1850 by Charles C. Whittelsey (1818-1889) to make upright drills, hand lathes and Walbridge patent engine lathes (below).

WICACO SCREW & MACHINE CO., Philadelphia, PA

Formed by Charles Parham about 1880 to make turret lathes/screw machines such as shown in the 1885 advertisement below. Light duty machines, they were primarily for brass workers. The firm continued in business through WWII. *(continued on next page)*

WIGHT & POWELL, Worcester, MA

A partnership of Joseph H. Wight and Albert M. Powell formed March 1, 1881, to make 18" engine lathes such as shown below. Wight left the firm later in 1881 and Powell reorganized as A.M. POWELL & CO.

NEW EIGHTEEN-INCH ENGINE LATHE

WILEY, NATHANIEL, Watertown, NY

Maker, in 1830, of the 22", wooden bed, rack drive lathe shown below. It was in use until 1889.

WILKINSON, DAVID, Pawtucket, RI

In 1794 Wilkinson (1771-1852) developed a screw-cutting lathe with slide rest (below), which he patented December 14, 1798, (Fig.). Wilkinson has a claim as an inventor of the slide rest and was certainly the first American to build a lathe with the device.

His first model was not successful, but in 1806 the Slater family erected a factory in Pomfret, CT, which made improved Wilkinson lathes.

Although Wilkinson never made lathes in commercial quantities, he is considered by many to be the father of the U.S. machine tool industry. Certainly, his early associates, who included Edward Bancroft and James S. Brown, went on to make major contributions to metal cutting lathe design.

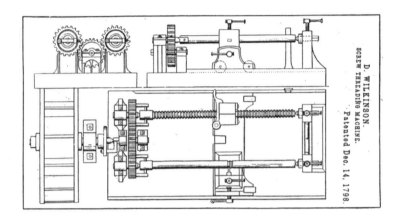

WILLARD MACHINE & TOOL CO., Cincinnati, OH

Formed in 1906 by George A. Willard (1858-1934) to make engine lathes, including the 13" model shown below. The firm reorganized as the Willard Machine Tool Co. in 1917.

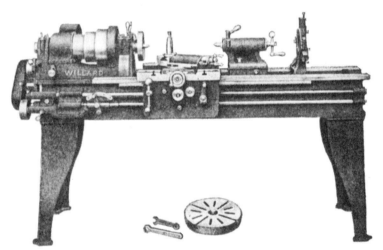

WINDSOR MACHINE CO., Windsor, VT

Formed in 1888 by Gilbert A. Davis, who served as president until he left in 1902. George O. Gridley (1869-1956) joined the firm in 1897 and developed the GRIDLEY automatic screw machine in 1902. The firm was bought by POTTER & JOHNSTON in 1911 but continued operation as WINDSOR MACHINE CO. until it was sold to the NATIONAL ACME CO. in 1915.

In 1889, the firm bought the assets of lathe maker JOHN BIRKENHEAD and offered his engine lathes, in slightly modified form (Fig.1), for a few years. Turret lathes and screw machines soon became the primary products, however.

Production in 1891 included screw machines/turret lathes in several sizes, included No. (Fig.2) and No. 4 (Fig.3). The MERCER turret lathe (Fig.4), offered in 16", 18", and 21" swing, was introduced in 1892.

The company's 1899 catalog offered 15" universal monitor lathes (Fig.5), 15" brass finisher's lathes, 25" chucking lathes (Fig.6), monitor lathes (Fig.7) in 13", 16" and 18" sizes, and screw machines in 9" (Fig.8) and 13" sizes. *(continued on next two pages)*

Fig.1

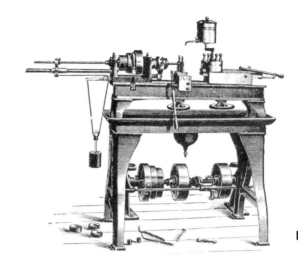

Fig.2

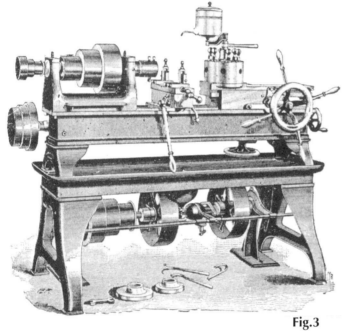

Fig.3

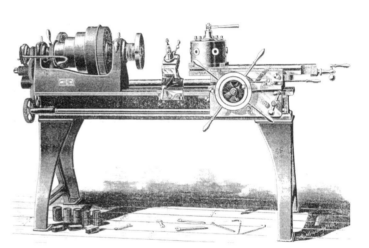

Fig.4

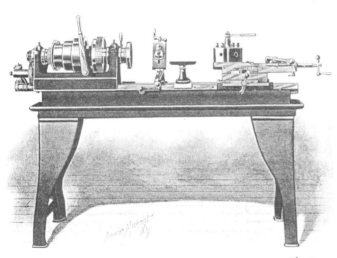

Fig.5

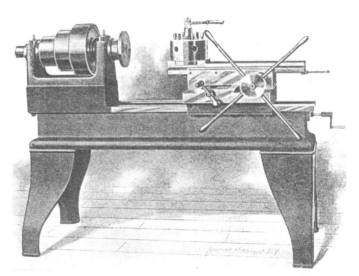

Fig.6

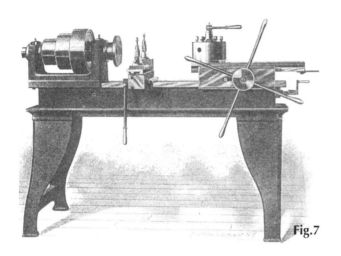

Fig.7

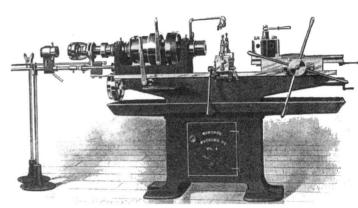

Fig.8

WINDSOR MFG. CO., Windsor, VT

Formed in 1865 by Ebenezer B. Lamson (1814-1892) and his son Eastborne E. Lamson as a reorganization of E.G. LAMSON & CO. Henry D. Stone continued as superintendent.

Maker of quarrying machinery and a variety of other machines, including turret lathes and engine lathes based on Frederick W. Howe and Henry D. Stone designs originally developed for ROBBINS & LAWRENCE and also made by E.G. LAMSON & CO.

An advertising broadsheet issued in 1865 illustrates back-geared engine lathes (Fig.1), another style of engine lathe "any size made to order" (Fig.2), hand lathes, and a "screw milling machine" (Fig.3), which was its name for the Howe turret lathe/screw machine.

In 1869, the firm reorganized as JONES, LAMSON & CO., with Russell L. Jones as the senior partner.

Fig.1

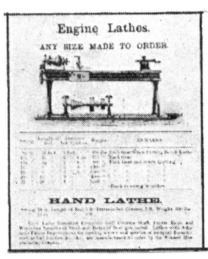

Fig.2

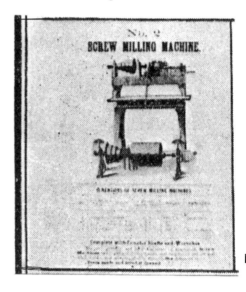

Fig.3

WINN, A.C., Boston, MA

Maker, in 1881, of bench lathes in combination (Fig.1) and turret (Fig.2) styles.

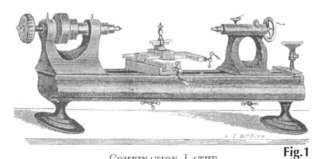

COMBINATION LATHE.   Fig.1

LATHE WITH TURRET HEAD.   Fig.2

WOOD, AURIN, Worcester, MA

Aurin Wood (1812-1896) left the WOOD & LIGHT MACHINE CO. about 1875 to operate under his own name. Products included 15", 18" and 20" engine lathes.

WOOD, CHARLES, Worcester, MA, later
WOOD & BALLARD, Worcester, MA

Formed in 1867 when Charles Wood left the partnership of BLAISDELL & WOOD. He operated alone until 1869 when he was joined by Charles M. Ballard and formed WOOD & BALLARD.

Products included engine lathes, hand lathes, planers, drilling machines and other machine tools.

WOOD, JENNISON & CO., Worcester, MA

A partnership of Aurin Wood (1812-1896) and S.S. Jennison formed in 1880 as a reorganization of the WOOD & LIGHT MACHINE CO. The firm specialized in shafting lathes.

WOOD, LIGHT & CO., Worcester, MA, later
WOOD & LIGHT MACHINE CO., Worcester, MA

A partnership of Aurin Wood (1812-1896) and Joseph F. Light formed in 1852 as a reorganization of WOODBURN, LIGHT & CO. The firm reorganized as a stock company, the WOOD & LIGHT MACHINE CO. in 1874. Light was replaced by S.S. Jennison in 1880 and the firm became WOOD, JENNISON & CO.

Production in 1870 included 16" engine lathes (Fig.1), 84" engine lathes (Fig.2), 100" engine lathes (Fig.3), and shafting lathes in 20", 24" and 28" swings (Fig.4). In 1872 it introduced its improved patent axle lathe (Fig.5). *(continued on next page)*

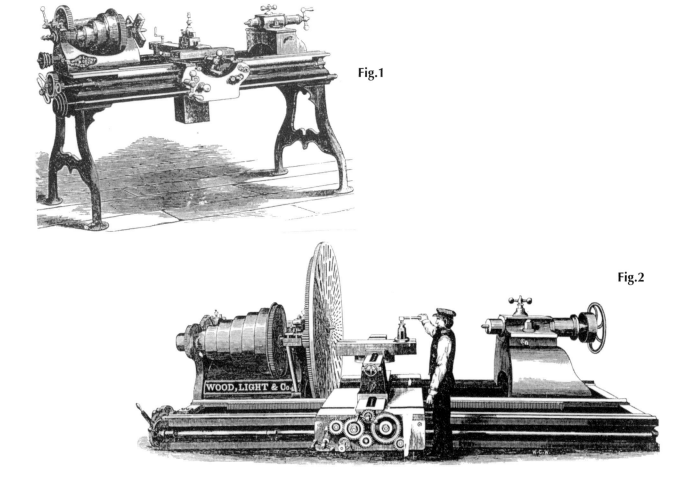

Fig.1

Fig.2

LATHE, - - - Twenty feet led, Swings eighty-four inches.

189

Fig.3

LATHE, - - - Twenty feet Bed, Swings one hundred inches.

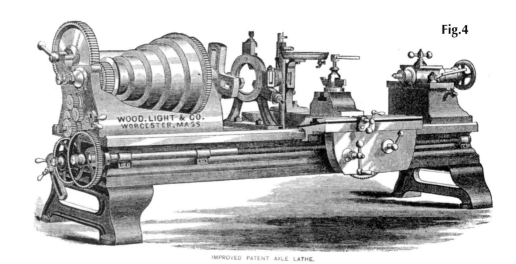

Fig.4

IMPROVED PATENT AXLE LATHE.

Fig.5

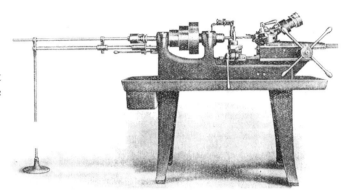

WOOD TURRET MACHINE CO., Brazil, IN

Founded in 1907 by David W. Wood. Wood's sole product appears to have been his own design of monitor lathes, later called the "tilted turret" lathe. Wood sold out in 1924.

WOODBURN, LIGHT & CO., Worcester, MA

A partnership of Josiah Woodburn, Joseph Light, John Williams, and Charles Wood, formed in 1846 to make engine and hand lathes and other machine tools. Woodburn left the firm in 1852 and was replaced by Aurin Wood. The firm was then reorganized as WOOD, LIGHT & CO.

WOODMAN & PIKE, Lake Village, NH

Maker of foot lathes in 1871. "Best in the country."

WORCESTER MACHINIST TOOL CO., Worcester, MA

Founded in 1856 and managed by Samuel Flagg who had previously operated SAMUEL FLAGG & CO. Other members of the company were Dexter Flagg, Lemuel G. Mason, and Pierson Cowie. The firm made planers, engine lathes, chucking lathes and hand lathes through the Civil War.

WRIGHT & CO., S.C., Fitchburg, MA

A partnership of Sylvester C. Wright (1816-1880) and his son-in-law James L. Chapman, formed in 1864 to make large engine lathes. Wright had been a contractor at the LOWELL MACHINE SHOP in 1847 and a partner in the PUTMAN MACHINE CO. when it was formed in 1854.

On January 1, 1867, the firm reorganized as a stock company, the FITCHBURG MACHINE CO.

WRIGHT, JOHN H., Bridgeport, CT

Maker of lathes and planers, operating in 1882. He claimed to be using WOOD & LIGHT CO. patterns.

WRIGHT & LAWRENCE, Lowell, MA, later
WRIGHT, A.L., Lowell, MA

A partnership of Albion L. Wright and Benjamin Lawrence, formed to make woodworking machinery. In 1881 the partners began making engine lathes. By 1885, Lawrence had left and Wright was operating the firm under his own name. His sole product continued to be cngine lathes such as that shown in the 1885 advertisement at rght.

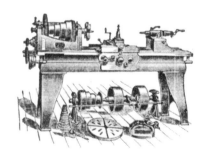

A. L. WRIGHT,
Manufacturer of ENGINE LATHES.
LOWELL, MASS.

YOUNG & CO., W.C., Worcester, MA, later
YOUNG MFG. CO., W.C., Worcester, MA, later
YOUNG MACHINE & TOOL CO., Worcester, MA

Founded by Willie C. Young (1849-1909) in 1879. Young was elected president when the firm incorporated as the W.C. YOUNG MFG. CO. in 1892. In 1907, the company again reorganized, as the YOUNG MACHINE & TOOL CO.; W.C. Young served as vice president until his death in 1909.

Young's first lathe was a 12" engine lathe (Fig.1) introduced in 1881. In 1882 he also offered a foot-power hand lathe (Fig.2) and a back-geared (Fig.3) hand lathe. An improved version of the 12" engine lathe (Fig.4) was introduced in 1886 and a screw cutting foot-power lathe (Fig.5) in 1888.

1897 production included 9" (Fig.6), 10" and 12" (Fig.7) foot-power lathes. Improved models of the foot-power lathes (Fig.8) and a 14" engine lathe (Fig.9) were introduced in 1898. *(continued on next page)*

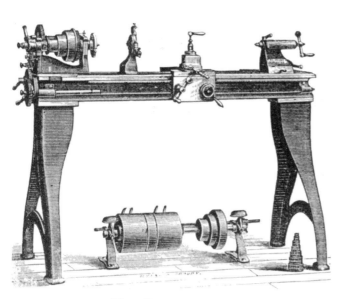

NEW ENGINE LATHE. **Fig.1**

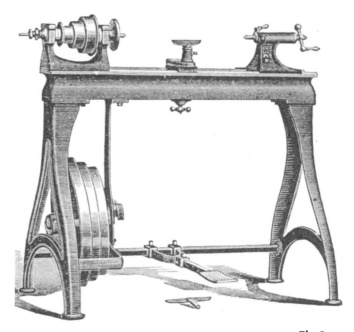

FOOT POWER HAND LATHE. **Fig.2**

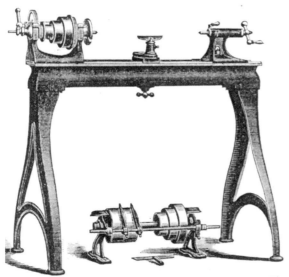

BACK-GEARED HAND LATHE. **Fig.3**

TWELVE-INCH ENGINE LATHE. **Fig.4**

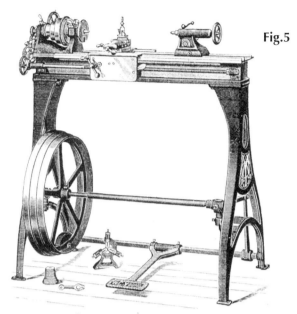

Fig.5

Fig.6

Screw Cutting Foot Lathe.

Fig.7

Fig.8

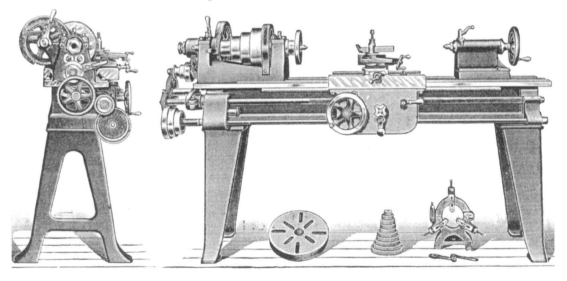

14-INCH ENGINE LATHE.

Fig.9